Maid
of the
Haystack

Martin J. Powell

 BRISTOL BOOKS

Bristol Books CIC, The Courtyard, Wraxall Hill,
Wraxall, Bristol BS48 1NA

Maid of the Haystack
written and researched by Martin Powell

Published by Bristol Books 2022

ISBN: 978-1-909446-34-2

Copyright: Bristol Books CIC

Design: Joe Burt

Martin Powell has asserted his right under the Copyright, Designs and
Patents Act of 1988 to be identified as the author of this work.

A CIP record for this book is available from the British Library.

Printed by TJ Books Limited.

Contents

This book is based on real events. Most of the characters and their actions are as described here, but some of the story is pure conjecture.

INTO THE
HAYSTACK

- Chapter One -

The Unexpected Visitor

IT IS A long hill out of Bristol on to the rolling downland at
Bedminster Down. Just as she reached the top of the hill and the
flatter downs stretched ahead of her, the old mare, Jessie, came to
a standstill and the cart she was pulling jerked to a halt. Sat up
high behind her, William Atkings appreciated she needed to rest
and spoke gently to her to acknowledge her efforts in getting them
out of the city and into the countryside. He looked at the track
ahead undulating across the open countryside and without thinking
slipped his hand beneath the horse blanket beside him and felt the
smooth reassuring butt of the one-shot pistol he had loaded before
leaving the city.

Gazing into the distance he could see the next, slightly
smaller, hill and he knew after that it was all level or downhill
for his journey home. There had been reports of highwaymen
and footpads operating in the area and he was prepared to at
least scare them with the gun if any appeared. Knowing what he
had under the sacking on the back of the cart made him feel a
little more vulnerable than usual. He was a fit, 30-year-old man,
well-acquainted with some of the, let's say, "less than honest"
men who frequented the Ship Tavern in Milk Street, Bristol, and
usually they paid him respect by not interfering with his business.
But there was a chance that today word had got around that his
cart was carrying a more valuable load than usual. Out of the
city, and in the empty country lanes, he felt more vulnerable.

Jessie's breathing was slowing and William took the
opportunity to look out to his right across the valley to the distant
hill of Failand. His eyes tracked the hill from left to right until
he saw the deep rift of the gorge through which the River Avon
flowed. The river was illuminated by sunlight and the lazy arms
of a windmill on the Bristol side shone as they turned, catching

9

the sun's rays. He breathed in the fresh air of the countryside, glad to be free of the smoke and dirt and grime of the city where he had spent his day. It was late summer and the hills were dotted with haystacks and hay ricks. He had spent most of last weekend building haystacks in his own village, along with his neighbours, ready for the winter. They stood at the far end of the valley he was now surveying, out of sight.

At the bottom of the valley he couldn't quite make out the road from Bristol that he usually took to get home. It was a flatter route home but today he had decided to come this way so he could drop down into Barrow Gurney and offload those items in his cart that had made the day so worthwhile. Somehow it seemed to be doubling back to take that lower road through Long Ashton then turn off to Barrow Gurney when so close to home. It was as he was musing on the view and waiting for Jessie to be ready to move on once again, that he noticed something unusual in the valley. At first he thought it was smoke from a fire. But then he realised it seemed to be moving along from right to left, almost certainly going along the road from Bristol towards his home, making its path clear even to him atop the distant hill. He pondered on it and wished he had one of the eyeglasses so popular with the sailors down at the docks so he could get the image closer and be sure of it. Relying on the naked eye, he concluded it must be a carriage, drawn by at least four horses. The speed and dust it was kicking up suggested it might even be six.

He pondered on whether it was Sir Jaritt Smith MP heading away from Ashton Court, the house that dominated the valley, who was now well-known for his connections with powerful folk in London. But it was not often Sir Jarrit headed South in that direction these days. Or maybe it was one of those crazy people who seemed to be trying to set new records every week for speedy journeys. It was said that some were taking not much more than 48 hours to get from Bristol to London with their slick teams flogging the horses to the maximum. Either way it was unusual on that road. At that speed it might well head for trouble when it hit the bends near his home at Flax Bourton unless the carriage driver knew the road intimately. More than one carriage had turned over in the last year on that bend. The thought of the horses on the carriage racing against time brought William back to Jessie and he noticed she was now itching to get going again, pawing with her hoof. So, he gently shook the reins and clicked his mouth twice and she started off once more.

Soon, William was lost in his own thoughts again and just concentrating on negotiating the ruts and stones along his route. In his prime at 30, he was regarded as a good-looking fellow by both men and women. His appeal was enhanced by the fact that he always seemed pretty calm and confident as he went about his day. Sooner than he expected he reached the finger post at the crossroads. One sign pointed left to Dundry, the other pointed right to Barrow Gurney and Jessie didn't really need to be told which way to go as the cart lurched to take the road down to the little village. Not that the finger post words meant anything to William. He knew a few letters of course. He signed his name "WA" on documents, instead of the usual "X", but reading wasn't something he was keen to pursue as an activity. It wasn't really for the likes of him, as he was always telling people.

Barrow Gurney wasn't much more than a handful of cottages clustered together beside the track in a little valley that was approached by a steep slope. Jessie pretty well knew where to stop outside the little cottage of Mary Collins. Mary brewed ale and served it from jugs in her back kitchen. It was nothing like the ale houses of the town and only those in the know made their way there to slake their thirst from the tankards that she kept for them. To be truthful Mary's brew varied in quality from week to week. Sometimes it could give you a fair gripe in the pit of the stomach, but it was worth the risk for the times when it was a wondrous nectar, smooth and clear and fine to quaff.

William busied himself about Jessie, who was already having a well-earned drink from the public horse trough as he tied her reins loosely to the post and ensured everything about the tack was tidy. Then he moved the pistol from under the blanket and hid it in a wooden box on the back of the cart before lifting the sacking and removing two heavy bags, which he swung over his shoulders before knocking on the door. William was a strong man, wiry and naturally fit from the physical work that he did every day. The bags would challenge an older man but he held them easily as he waited for the door to open.

Mary answered, smiled, and pulled the door back to give him access and he could tell from the sound of Somerset accents within that his three old friends were already there, already had their tankards filled and were deep into the business of the day.

"Here he be, the Boring Bastard of Bourton," said John Stokes and William smiled as his friends all chuckled at the irreverent greeting between friends.

"Oh Sod off," said William, "at least I've got something to bloody talk about at the end of the day. Not like thee with thee daily summary of life." He put on an affected voice: "Six in the morning milk a cow; five past six milk another cow; half past six think about milking another cow. Stand round for eight hours watching cows eat grass until it's time to milk another cow!"

Edward Cock, known as "Cripple", and Joseph Wilmot, known as "Willie", laughed at the banter aimed at the dairy farmer and the men poured some of Mary's ale into a tankard for William and they all settled around the kitchen table as William put his bags down on the flagstones.

"You got to admit," said John Stokes, not letting it go, "that you were pretty bloody boring the other day telling us about that house clearance you did in Stokes Croft. Christ, I think I know every trinket and glass they owned". The men laughed and Mary wagged her finger saying "no blasphemy" but the men hardly heard her in their raucousness and she rolled her eyes and turned to busy herself with the pots and pans.

"Well, I think you will be interested in this lot today," said William. Even though he knew that everyone around was trustworthy, and could be counted as friends, he couldn't help lowering his voice for dramatic effect and saying "silver" as he indicated the bags on the floor.

"I've been helping out with a probate inventory today and let's just say there are a number of items that haven't gone on the list. I gave a fair price for them but I think if you can get them down to Taunton or up to London there is a good profit to be made. One of those big houses down in St. Augustine's. Family just wanted shot of some of it as it was likely from privateering or slaving and there is a bit of heat now around where these sort of things come from. They don't want to sell it in the shops in town, rather we got rid of it for them and they make a bit of cash."

The men leaned forward interested as William started taking the items out one by one. Silver jugs, some plates, silver candlesticks, sugar tongs. They started passing them round looking at the maker's marks on them, each weighing up the value in their minds, both locally and in the markets, taverns and shops of Taunton and London.

Cripple Cock started sorting the items he thought might best suit his forthcoming trip South to Taunton while Willie Wilmot put aside those he thought might sell well in Bath. The men worked methodically with all agreeing on the star items that John Stokes would send up to London through his contacts.

William reached into the corner of the bag and pulled out a thick bundle of cloth and carefully started unwrapping it.

"What do you think?" he said, putting three glass goblets onto the table. Clear glass that you could see through and fine, very fine, they were delicate and clearly by a superior maker.

John Stokes made a little whistling noise then said, "I'd say Venetian Crystal without a doubt. Must be around 100 years old, say 1660 something like that. Now they are worth a pretty penny in the right place. Apart from some of the visitors to the Hot Well you aren't going to find those that appreciate them enough around here. London for sure. That was some probate you were at."

William Atkings had spent the afternoon with a small group cataloguing the belongings of a recently deceased merchant in the St Augustine's area near the City Docks. Of course William wasn't there to do the cataloguing. He was there to remove the items that the Merchant's family didn't want recorded. Items such as blankets, gallons of beer, cotton counterpanes and the like had been conscientiously recorded. But half a cartload of booty had been entrusted to Atkings, who ensured cash would be raised with his "contacts" making the items disappear and making a good turn on them at the same time.

"I might just keep this," said William, taking out a small handbell and ringing it for effect. Its tinkle was surprisingly loud for such a small delicate thing. "I can ring it to tell Amy I'm ready for my supper."

He laughed and Mary, listening in, retorted, "I expect you'd get that bell wrapped round your ear if Amy heard you say that." The little group of men laughed and again turned to start their business, dividing up the items between them and discussing the relative merits and best place for them to be sold.

Just a few miles away Amy Atkings was in the kitchen watching the first wisps of smoke from the fire she had lit climb up the back grate and creep into the chimney. There was a bit of flame and heat and she lifted the copper pot of slaw and meat she had been preparing on to the trivet.

She knew William would be on his way back from Bristol by now and it would take a while for the food to cook. It would be good for them to eat together now the haymaking was over and they had a little more time without worrying about the weather closing in. She saw the slaw start to bubble and just as she went to move the pot to ensure it had the maximum heat under the middle she heard the thundering of hooves in the lane outside the cottage. It sounded like a big carriage going by and she made her way to the front door which opened straight onto the road. By the time she got there the carriage was out of sight, the only evidence it had passed by being the dust flying in the late afternoon air. She made a face and looked across at the cottages opposite. No sign of Sarah Derrick, who lived there, coming to her door. So Amy turned back into her cottage, looked for a moment at the dirty exterior cottage walls that seemed to be a magnet for the mud and dirt from the road, then shut the door, taking the few steps back to the kitchen, which looked out on the backyard where the chickens were busy scratching and clucking and making their usual afternoon fuss. The slaw was bubbling away nicely now.

She reached down to the wooden bucket in readiness to collect water from the pump. Amy was at her happiest in the little cottage she and William called home. She wasn't that interested in venturing into the city much. She was a country girl at heart and liked the simple ways of the farms and small-holdings around Flax Bourton. The soil here was red with clay but it was good for growing. William was able to get into Bristol fairly easily to supplement their living with a bit of buying and selling and it meant that they were relatively well off compared to others around the village. Her only regret was that so far they had not been blessed with children.

She liked walking in the woods or through Bourton Combe, one of the natural limestone gorges that dotted the area. The oolite limestone made great building material for the houses and fallen branches from the yew, elder and elm trees could be collected up to go on the fire. Amy started humming a little tune to herself as she worked and her idle thoughts were interrupted by a rapping on the door.

She thought it was probably Sarah Derrick popping across to see if she has seen the carriage or maybe to borrow some implement or other for her own late afternoon cooking. The two women were constantly in and out of each other's homes. But it was unusual for her to tap in such a formal way…usually it would be a rap on the window and a shout of "oo-oo" to alert her good friend to her presence.

Taking up a cloth in her hand, Amy went to the front door and opened it. The smile froze on her face as she opened the door as it was not her friend Sarah Derrick but a woman she had never seen before in her life. The woman was tall, taller than most of the women she knew. She was elegant and wearing clothes more suitable for high society than for a rural life. She looked agitated. You might even say distracted. She was wringing her hands and moving from foot to foot and at first didn't make any eye contact with Amy.

Amy looked left and right along the lane and could see the woman was alone. No horse. No cart. No other person around. The woman was wearing a long fine dress and a coat that was a little too warm for the season. When she looked the woman in the face she saw that she was beautiful, quite the most exquisite face she had ever seen. Dark brown eyes looking out from under black curly hair that fell in natural ringlets about her shoulders. Her face was thin, with prominent cheekbones and pale, not ruddy-faced like those of her friends and neighbours. She didn't look as if she had spent much of her life outside. Her eyes seemed constantly dancing or cast down.

Amy spoke: "Can I help you?" The question at last made the woman focus her eyes on Amy and she shuffled from foot to foot a few more times before answering. "Sorry…I….I'm sorry… umm…do you?…I mean…have you milk?"

Amy could see the stranger was not comfortable and her mind was racing on how such a beautiful creature - for the more she looked at her the more striking and elegant she appeared - could possibly have arrived on her doorstep in such a sorry state. She beckoned the woman in and held the door open. The woman picked up a large bag that was behind her and stepped just inside the door but stopped immediately as if she did not want to impose or over-step her welcome.

Amy saw the bag was of a good quality, the sort that might be sold in London and be used by the women at the Hot Well, or by guests of Sir Jarrit Smith at Ashton Court. Maybe this lady was a visitor to the Smith estate. Or maybe she was a friend of the Gore family who lived in Barrow Court and were related to the Smith's by marriage. The families had thrived recently with the coal shafts being sunk below Bedminster Down - black gold they were calling it. Perhaps she had wandered out of Barrow Court and got lost.

Amy kept an eye on the stranger, who was still looking agitated and uncomfortable as she took a little milk from a jug and poured it into a cup and offered it to her. The woman nodded in appreciation and drank it thirstily.

"What are you doing around here? Where are you headed?" asked Amy, hoping to get some light thrown on all the speculative questions in her head.

"I...um...passing...thank you. Thank you, milk," said the woman nodding and Amy perceived from the few words a peculiar accent she hadn't heard before. Maybe the woman was from up country, perhaps even foreign. She seemed to have problems searching for the right words. With that she handed Amy the cup, quickly picked up the bag and headed back out into the road.

"Are you all right?" Amy shouted after her, partly concerned for the woman's safety but at the same time a little offended that she hadn't offered to pay for the hospitality. Not that she wanted any money for the kindness but it would have been polite to have at least feigned proffering some coins for the drink. Amy stood on the doorstep and saw the woman wander towards Farleigh, away from Bristol. Her bag seemed heavy and she shifted it from hand to hand. She didn't look as if she could walk far and somehow didn't have the look of someone who had walked a long way to get here. As the woman disappeared from view around the bend in the road Amy shook her head again, looked across at Sarah Derrick's cottage and decided to cross over to see her.

"Ooo-oo" she shouted as she reached the cottage and in seconds Sarah was at the door with a cloth and pot in her hand that she was in the middle of wiping.

"Did you see that woman?" Amy asked. "Just knocked on my door bold as brass and asked for milk. She was very fine. Dressed like a lady."

"No I didn't see her. I've been out the back most of the day with Johnny. Did she have a carriage?" asked Sarah.

"No, that's just it. She seemed to be walking. Very peculiar I tell thee. Perhaps she's wandered a little too far from the Hot Well. There are some weird types getting down there these days by all accounts. London types!"

The two women laughed and both looked up the road hoping to catch a last glimpse of the woman. But she was gone. Little Johnny Derrick came out to the door to hold on to his mother's apron and peer up at the neighbour from across the road, listening intently to the two women.

"I've never seen her around here before," said Amy, "can't imagine where she thinks she is going to get wandering down there."

The two women exchanged pleasantries for a few moments but both knew they had domestic tasks to carry out and without any formal goodbyes made their way back into their cottages.

Back inside, the pot was bubbling vigorously and Amy went over to the fire to shift the trivet to make sure it wouldn't boil over. She took the wooden bucket out into the yard and walked along the stone slab lane to the pump. Placing the bucket underneath the pump she took hold of the handle with both hands. The first few heaves on the handle were always hard as the air sucked through the pump but then the water began to flow and it was a smooth easy movement and Amy was able to look up from her task and across the fields towards Naylsey. The haystacks were standing proud, testament to the work of the village over the last few weeks. Everyone helped each other at haymaking time and the five haystacks on their smallholding had been created not just by Amy and William but by Sarah Derrick and her husband and at least 12 others from the village joining when they could. In return they would help with harvesting on the other farms and small-holdings in the area. There was a little contention with some families but generally harvest time was good in Flax Bourton with everyone mucking in together.

As the water gushed in spurts into the bucket Amy saw something move in a field over between the haystacks and she stopped for a moment so her eyes could focus on the distant movement. Yes, she was sure of it. It was the woman who had asked for the milk. She was wandering in the fields, still hauling the bag she was carrying from shoulder to shoulder. She was following the winding tracks that the haymakers had made. Amy shook her head and started to resume the task of filling the wooden bucket…a few more pumps and it was as heavy as she could carry. She hoisted it up and looked again. The distant figure had gone. Obviously heading across the fields towards Naylsey, maybe trying to find a way back to the road that led out to the coast.

Amy turned and carried the water back into her home. She knew William would be home soon and the most important thing was for them to have something to eat together after a long day.

Cripple Cock and Willie Wilmot were saying their goodbyes in the road in Barrow Gurney as William untied Jessie from the post and prepared her for the short journey home. John Stokes was already halfway up Hobbs Lane with his sack of booty heading homeward as William finally clambered up onto his cart and, waving to the two men, still engaged in a bit of banter as they slowly moved apart to go to their homes at opposite ends of the village. The hedges on each side were high but William could just see over them and soon they gave way as he passed the mill race with a few ducks floating on the water and the familiar undulations of the lane that he must have driven Jessie down more than a hundred times.

Before he knew it they were at the crossroads and he turned left for the final little twisting climb into Flax Bourton. He could see the smoke from the cottage chimney and knew that Amy was cooking something good. The ale in his belly had given him an appetite as he swung the cart into the yard alongside the house. He released the straps one by one as Jessie stood patiently, then when she was finally free he patted her and said "good girl" and she walked of her own accord to the gate, which he opened and she was pleased to trot into her paddock and started chewing on some grass and a little hay that Amy had put into the stone trough earlier.

William pulled the cart by the shafts and put it in its usual place then reached into the box and pulled out the small pistol. He carefully walked a few yards from the cottage door and knocked the small ball of metal onto a stone then discharged the gun, pointing it at a bush as the flash in the pan rang out. Jessie jumped and made a whinnying noise. The back door flew open and Amy stood there with a look of disapproval on her face.

"Do you have to load that gun?" she asked, crossing her arms.

"Well there's a welcome!" said William, smiling. "Sadly these days it isn't safe coming back from Bristol without it. If it isn't the bloody footpads, it's people dragging every fit man they can find off to fight in the Americas."

William checked the gun over before retrieving the ball from the stone and placing it in a leather pouch with others. He wrapped the gun in the pouch of ammunition and walked into the house, stowing it just inside the door in a small wooden box with other tools and bits and pieces that he called his own.

Amy had calmed down and he looked at the soft outline

of her rump as she bent over to pick up the pan. He knew she wouldn't be mad at him for long. He was staring at her and could feel that surge of excitement he felt whenever Amy, his Amy, was nearby and being feisty. She felt his eyes on her and looked around and caught his stare.

"What?", she said, but her attempt at feigning anger at him was betrayed by the corners of her mouth, which just couldn't help but turn up in a smile at the rugged, hungry, work-worn man looking at her. He saw the smile and that was the signal for him to go over and put his arms around her, feeling her clothing move beneath his rough hands and enjoying the shape and smoothness of her. She straightened, turned and their lips met in a long lingering kiss.

She broke away, putting her hands on his chest, and he sat down at the table ready to enjoy the food she had prepared and looking forward to their time together later when the sun dipped and the candles were lit and the long country night was under way.

Amy put out the plates and he watched her as she was surrounded by steam and started ladling from the pot she had taken from the fire. He took off his boots and enjoyed the pleasure of his feet relaxing on the flagstones of his home. He reached into his pocket and just as Amy finished plating their tea he rang the little handbell and its cheerful tinkle rang out around the cottage making Amy jump with a start.

"Dinner is served!" he announced and Amy fell into fits of laughter. "Where did you get that?" she asked, "I suppose that's the sort of thing they use at Ashton Court for their fancy guests!"

"It came from a fine house in Bristol. I've been helping with some probate there. While the team were writing things down I did a deal to remove some of the items for cash. Saw the boys in Barrow Gurney, but thought this might be fun to keep. Maybe I can tinkle it when I expect a special bit of service from you?" His eyes were on her and she knew that look. In fact she loved that look.

"Eat your so called dinner," she said. They sat down opposite each other and started on their meal, both enjoying being together in their little cottage home after a busy day.

As they picked up their cutlery to eat, Amy remembered the strange visitor this afternoon and decided to tell William about her.

"Hey, talking of fancy guests at Ashton Court, I had a young girl dressed in some finery knock on the door earlier and ask for milk. She wasn't from round here. She was beautiful but I'm not sure she was completely all there. She spoke funny. Might have been foreign or might have been from up country. Lovely hair and eyes though and a dress that nobody on farming wage could afford. I think I saw her wandering across the fields at the back later."

"Across the field?" exclaimed William. "Where on earth was she going? There have been a lot of people down at the Hot Well lately with their fancy ways, paying over the odds for some starch for their hair but they don't usually get this far."

Amy laughed. William had a friend who had a good little racket going mixing lavender with starch at a little factory in Bristol. William was making a pretty penny from delivering starch to the Hot Well on his cart so that the men and women who enjoyed the waters could powder their wigs and hair with it, as was their fashion. He enjoyed the occasional little glimpse into the world of finery and in fact always fitted in well with those who some might assume were his betters. That was what Amy loved about William, he seemed to fit in wherever he went and everyone seemed to instantly like him. He never talked down to anyone but he was never subservient either and it didn't matter whether it was a pauper, a reverend or a Duke, William spoke to them the same and they seemed to react to his easy manner with them.

Amy thought about the girl, wondering where she might be

heading and seeing the sun streak through from across the field, low in the sky. She wondered just how far she was going to get before the darkness of the night was on her.

The sun set low over the Bristol Channel near Clevedon and its rays turned the fields and hay ricks of the Somerset countryside a bright golden hue. It made for an extra hour or so of daylight in the valley compared to other villages not far away that were in the shadow of the Mendip Hills. That extra hour was one of the reasons so many villages had grown up close to each other. That light and the soil that made growing relatively easy so that farmers and market gardeners could grow not only enough for themselves but a little extra to sell. The villagers around Flax Bourton, Farleigh, West Town and Barrow Gurney were not rich, but they were not poor either. William and Amy were fairly typical of the local population.

But 1776 had brought worries about the future. The nearby city of Bristol was changing, and not necessarily for the better. The corporation seemed determined to fleece the populous with tolls and taxes, the docks were often a dangerous place with many saying the once-thriving port would not survive as the tidal range didn't suit the new ships that docked there and most of the big business going to Liverpool. Even in sleepy Flax Bourton people knew that the situation in America, where a revolution had broken out, was hitting them hard.

The world seemed a much smaller place than it had ever been to Amy and William in the past. Tobacco pipes made in Bristol for America lay unsold and unshipped - William had picked up some boxes and had been able to sell them by sending them through John Stokes to London. All manner of goods that just a few years ago would have sailed off to America were now lying in warehouses around Bristol Docks. Some people had gone off to fight and there were plenty of stories of men and boys who had too much to drink and found themselves taken off to fight in America.

The local MP Sir Jarrit Smith had received his knighthood for being a supporter of the Prime Minister and most local people respected him for the way he represented the area. The fact his estate was close by meant that those in Flax Bourton somehow felt they had influence on national and international things - there was always someone who could have a word with Sir Jarrit. It was surprising how far his influence seemed to extend.

Amy worried most nights. She worried about America; she worried about Bristol; she worried about pirates. There was also a growing number of people saying that the selling of African slaves to America was wrong. It all didn't feel right any more. The more she got to know about the way the world worked the more she longed for the simple rural times of her childhood when the world didn't seem such a small place and where America, slavery, pirates and the like seemed far away.

There was such a golden light in the fields that Amy and William decided to take a walk together after washing down their meal with some milk. There were a few last pieces of waste straw in the far field to pick up. They would be brought back and used in Jessie's small stable to soak up some of her mess. Mixed with straw the horse dung would then be put back onto the land. It was a simple task to pick it up that they could do with little urgency and enjoy the last rays of the sun as they did so.

It was a beautiful evening and the hay ricks were positively glowing as they reached the end field with their forks. Amy started raking and William checked the hedge line. They worked silently moving everything into a heap so that it could be gathered up. Every minute was precious as the sun was now dipping quickly and the light turning from bright yellow to almost orange.

Amy stood to look at the view and it was then she spotted movement in one of the hay ricks and saw that there was straw on the floor in front of it where yesterday it had looked so neat. She looked over at William but he was still totally absorbed in his task and had noticed nothing.

She walked towards the haystack and stopped suddenly. She could hear singing. A woman's voice, soft tones, not a song that Amy knew. She couldn't make out the words. Maybe they were foreign, maybe the woman was simply humming the tune and didn't really know the words. But it was singing all right. It was singing and it was coming from the haystack.

Amy went back towards William and he looked up as she approached. She said nothing but her face and her finger-pointing was enough. She signalled the haystack and he carefully made his way to stand alongside her.

"Listen" she hissed. There it was again. The soft lilting voice of a woman. She sounded happy. The little entrancing song wafting on the gentle breeze towards them as the sun dipped lower and the world turned to an enchanting, magical golden colour and the sky reddened in a beautiful Somerset sunset. It was a scene that a master of painting would love to capture. Perfect in its simplicity and beauty.

The couple inched nearer. As they rounded the haystack they saw her. It was the woman who had asked for the milk. She was bathed in golden sunlight, her black hair tumbling over bare shoulders. Her blouse was hanging from a stick pushed into the hay. She was bare-breasted, small breasts but the large brown nipples were a feast for William's eyes. The woman's back was arched. On her lower half she wore the same fine dress that she had been wearing earlier but it had been pulled down so that the top hung from her waist. Her midriff was flat and shining golden in the sunlight. The lilting, haunting song on her lips seemed to only enhance her amazing beauty.

For a few seconds the young couple just stood transfixed at this vision in their haystack. Then Amy saw that William was gaping at the beautiful curves of this other woman and felt she had to speak and act.

"Excuse me," she said. Startled, the girl drew up the straps of her dress to cover most of her modesty and grabbed the blouse, holding it in front of herself. She seemed to be in a panic looking around her as if assessing whether it was possible to gather up the belongings around her and run. She was frantically looking from one object to another but the suddenness with which her evening had been interrupted just seemed to leave her in a panic of inaction. Eventually she turned her back and quickly pulled on her blouse and turned nervously and frightened to face the pair.

Amy noticed how the woman's eyes shone in the light of the sunset and how fine her skin looked and how beautiful her hair was. She was nothing like any of the country girls around here.

"What are you doing here?" Amy asked. "This is our haystack. Where have you come from?"

The woman looked confused for a moment then answered in the same faltering voice as before, back at the cottage. "I sleep here....ummmm. thank you for the milk...I sleep here and then I go tomorrow."

"You want to sleep here?" said William. "Have you nowhere else to go?"

"I sleep here. I have come a long way. Thank you for the milk. I don't want to be any problem to you nice people". The woman seemed to be growing in confidence and although she had an accent they didn't recognise they could see that she was distressed and it seemed a simple case of someone who needed a bed for the night.

"Where were you trying to get to for tonight? Can we help at all?" said William.

"I will just sleep here and then go on in the morning," said the woman and then once again said, "thank you for the milk".

William and Amy went closer and the woman sat still in a little hollow she had made in the haystack. They saw that she had spread out some belongings from the bag she was carrying. A bowl of water was by her side and it now seemed obvious that she had washed her blouse and had been drying it on the branch in the sun. William noticed how the material stuck to her skin where it was still damp after she had put it on.

Amy sat down next to the woman and offered her hand. "What's your name dear?"

"Louisa, my name is Louisa," she answered, smiling and reaching out to touch the hand of the woman who had been kind to her. She added, "Thank you for the milk".

Amy laughed: "I think you have thanked us enough for the milk now. Look, why don't you come back to the house and we can perhaps find room for you there. It is a beautiful evening but it is going to turn cold as soon as the sun dips below the horizon."

"No, I sleep here." said Louisa, looking slightly agitated at the invitation, a reaction that Amy really didn't understand. But there was something noble and honest about the woman squatting in the haystack, even if she did appear to have some problems with communicating with people. William came close too and the couple reassured the stranger that if she wanted to stay in the haystack she could. Each time they said how much more comfortable it would be to come back into the house Louisa seemed to get distressed and it was easier to change the subject and let her calm down again.

They sat there for maybe 30 minutes as the sun dipped and the moon came out and they learned little about Louisa apart from her name. She said she had come a long way but she seemed very hazy on where she had started that journey and seemed to have little idea about where she was going.

As they talked with her it became obvious she was not going to move so William started to build a little barrier using the hay between Louisa and the prevailing wind. He also found some softer hay in which she could make herself comfortable and showed her how she might bed down.

All the time, Amy and Louisa talked; Amy asking questions and Louisa saying little but politely but firmly saying she wanted to stay the night in the haystack and would leave in the morning.

Soon a flick of cold air blowing around their necks told the couple it was time to head back to the cottage. Louisa had settled down and was looking a little weary and they were convinced she would soon be asleep in the little den that William had made for her. Amy felt that she had a new, if slightly strange, friend, to stay.

As they walked back hand in hand to ensure they did not lose their footing in the diminishing light, William asked, "What do you reckon. Is she a dumbledoodle?"

Amy screwed up her face, "I don't know. I think she might be foreign. I think that's why she seems a bit slow at times. But she's clearly been through something. I can't imagine how she ended up here. Did she walk here? Her clothes are more London than Bristol. I've only seen those kinds of clothes on the finest visitors to Ashton Court or Barrow Court. Do you think she has wandered out from there and just got lost? Maybe one of those foreign visitors that they have over from time to time. They have plantations and slaves and fancy contacts all over Europe."

Back at the cottage the night had finally fallen and William lit the candles around the place and finally changed out of his work clothes. He put on his cotton nightshirt that buttoned at the neck. Amy washed and put on an old pair of cotton bloomers and a little frilly cotton top that she knew revealed a lot of her bosom. The flickering candles around the cottage cast their intimate light and the couple slid into bed next to each other.

Soon their hands were exploring each other's familiar bodies. Amy was hoping that maybe this time they would be blessed with the son or daughter she so craved. She felt a thrill rush through her as they took to the bed together. They had been husband and wife now for three years. Nobody had ever meant so much to her and turned her on like him and she felt they were a match made in heaven. Since the first moment he had spoken to her at the May Fair she knew they were made for each other.

William leaned into his wife. He closed his eyes. In his mind's eye he could see the soft back of Louisa. Her small but perfectly formed breasts and the nipples. The nipples. The dark round brown nipples. He felt Amy responding to him. He thought again...the black hair shining in the sun, the hands so delicate grabbing at the muslin blouse, he pictured the blouse wet upon her skin, revealing the hard nipple and the eyes... oh the brown eyes...he could hold back no more. Amy gripped hold of her husband as the small wooden bed shook and quivered and the candles on the small bedside table flickered and spluttered at the vibration.

Chapter Two

Dumbledoodle

THE FIRST MORNING light into the valley turned the night from black to a dirty grey. It slowly illuminated the hedgerows and slid through the small windows of the cottages bringing morning to the bedroom walls. The light was the signal for the first chirrup. The complex musical flute-like notes of the blackbird struck up firm and clear and the music seemed to waken other birds. The blackbird's voice could be heard throughout Flax Bourton signalling the end of the darkness and crept into the ears of anyone not fully asleep and tucked under the blankets. Smaller birds began to join in as the light grew stronger and the day began.

The robin joined in with his song and soon there was chirruping and warbling and a cacophony of sounds. Beautiful and strange and loud across the valley as the birds celebrated a new day and began to scurry out of the bushes, shake their feathers and take their places in the trees.

The noise grew louder and louder in direct relation to the light rising and illuminating the scene. The fields of hay ricks had a wisp of morning mist between them and the whole scene looked colder and fresher than the soft rich colours of the night before when the sun had disappeared over the horizon.

Louisa lay in the folds of hay and could hardly believe the sound. It was surely paradise. Birds celebrating life. Birds chirruping, calling, exclaiming, tweeting, making as much noise as their small bodies could possibly make. The sound grew and grew like an orchestra tuning up for a magnificent concert. Each one seemingly knowing when its contribution would add maximum effect to the growing, enchanting, rich melodious musical sound.

Amy was awake and heard it too. William's arm still lay heavy across her and the gentle sounds of his regular breathing were drowned out by the birds just outside the window. The birds were waking up the people of Somerset, calling them to greet the new dawn. The freshness of the new day blew through the valley and entered the gaps in the window frames, taking away the acrid smell of last night's fires and the stale smell of the burned wax of the candles, and replacing them with the sweetness of the countryside air.

After a few moments lying listening to the familiar dawn chorus Amy gently lifted William's arm away and slid out of bed. She shoved her feet into clogs and put her long coat on over her nightgown, went to the back door and out into the air and around the bushes to where William had constructed the latest soil pit, enclosed in sail cloth he had brought home from Bristol. She sat on the little wooden seat he had constructed and listened to the birds some more as she went about her morning routine.

She thought of Louisa in the haystack and went back into the house. In one of the cupboards was a chamber pot that belonged to her mother that they rarely used. She usually only got it out when someone was ill and unable to get out to the soil pit. It had some decorative flowers around the rim and was a little fancy for everyday use, but not valuable. She felt it was appropriate for their elegant, if unexpected, visitor.

The clouds were scudding across the sky but it looked as if it would be a dry day today. Amy carried the pot to the haystack and found Louisa still buried in the straw lying on her back, wide awake and looking at the sky.

She smiled and greeted Amy, saying, "It is very nice here. The birds have been welcoming me to this place. Such a beautiful place. You are lucky to live here."

Amy smiled; she loved the area too and wouldn't want to live anywhere else. Not that she had much knowledge of anywhere else. She had once travelled North to Gloucester and visited the magnificent Cathedral there and as a girl she had gone to Porlock with her parents to visit a relative and had some memories of steep hills, spectacular cliffs and a sea bluer than you ever find in Clevedon.

She handed the chamber pot to Louisa, who with little ceremony climbed out of her place in the haystack and squatted upon it. When she had finished she handed the bowl of steaming, warm piss to her companion, saying, "Thank you".

It was such a strange action that Amy didn't at all take offence, but instead started giggling to herself as she walked across to the small brook that, with the bushes, formed a natural border for the field and emptied the chamber pot there.

If that had been William or anyone else, she would probably have said something like "What did your last servant die from? Overwork?" But she didn't know Louisa well enough to chastise her and also somehow, with her beautiful clothing and elegant ways, she seemed superior, like a lady, even though she was showing all the signs of being a homeless wanderer.

Louisa was making herself comfortable in the haystack again when Amy got back from emptying the pot. Now was the time to find out more from her.

"Where are you travelling on to?" she asked casually. It was clear that Louisa had heard but she didn't answer and instead angled her head downwards and pretended to be particularly interested in one stalk of hay.

"Have you any plans for today?" asked Amy, trying again.

"No plans. I stay here. I like it here," said Louisa. She looked at Amy and gave her a big beaming smile. She did, indeed, seem to be very comfortable in the haystack. She seemed more assured and settled than last night. As the grey dawn turned into full sunlight Amy saw again just how beautiful Louisa was. Her dark hair was striking. Her eyes were engaging, especially when she smiled and her hands showed no signs of ever having wielded a scythe or washed any clothes or scrubbed away at floors until they were red raw.

"How far have you travelled?" asked Amy, again trying to get some information out of the stranger.

"Very far," said Louisa, for a moment looking as if she might just say something more. Then she checked herself and said once again, "Very far", With those words she lay back on the hay and started looking at the sky and began singing the song she had been singing the night before when Amy approached her.

"What is that song?" said Amy. But there was no reply, just more singing and Amy stood there awkwardly for a moment or two before picking up the empty chamber pot and heading back to the house, her emotions a mixture of exasperation, amusement and compassion for the girl, who clearly had some kind of problem.

William was in the kitchen standing in just his nightshirt when she got back to the cottage. He had lit the fire and put a pot of water on.

"That girl is not quite right in the head," Amy said as she greeted her husband. "She doesn't seem to know where she is going or where she has come from. She says she is going to stay in the haystack today."

William replied as he went about his morning routine, "I'll go and talk to her before I go into Bristol. Do you think she has had a bang to the head or something? Maybe she is staying at Barrow Court or Ashton Court and has somehow ended up out here after an accident or something. I can't believe someone in clothes like that is living rough. She looks like a princess or the wife of some rich merchant or something. We don't get many like her around here."

William went outside and picked up some eggs from the chicken run and brought them in and put them in the pot on the fire.

"I took her a chamber pot. She pissed in it and handed it back to me to empty," said Amy, "I think she might be used to servants!"

William laughed. "I bet you told her where to go." Amy

looked at her feet. She was thinking. Morning hunger pangs were upon her and that made her think about their visitor.

"Who's going to feed her sitting in that haystack? We haven't got much here and I've no time or inclination to cook for her," said Amy.

William took control. He knew his wife would really want to help out the stranger. That was the sort of person she was. But he also knew that she would fret about what was the right thing to do.

"Don't worry about it. Leave it to me. I'll talk to her and try to get some sense out of her. If I can't then I'll ask up at Barrow Court and Ashton Court and put the word out she is here. Someone will come for her pretty soon I would think."

So, mid-morning, William led a little delegation of his wife, Sarah Derrick and her young son, and they trooped down towards the haystack. Sarah brought a little bread and Amy had some milk with little Johnny trooping along behind, just carrying a stick. Before setting off they had talked for a few moments in Amy's kitchen about the girl. Sarah was fascinated to meet her.

At the haystack it was as if nothing had happened since last time Amy saw her. Louisa was still lying on her back staring up at the sky, humming the little tune to herself. Her dress was spread out over the hay, some of which was now sticking in her hair, rendering her even more attractive.

The large bag she had been carrying, still bulging with things, was thrown carelessly on the ground next to her. She sat up when she heard them coming, looked a little worried at first then looked at the faces of Amy and William and smiled.

"My friends," she said, welcoming them. It was as if this was her home and she was greeting some unexpected visitors that had turned up.

She beamed at Johnny. "Little boy," she said and Johnny beamed back and climbed up next to her in the hay. Sarah Derrick was pop-eyed and slack-jawed at the woman. Although

Amy had described her it was still something of a surprise to find someone who looked like a regular lady perched in the haystack like this.

Amy handed over some milk and Sarah passed her the bread and Louisa consumed it as Amy introduced Sarah. They fell into conversation about the bread and the milk and Louisa seemed quite calm and content and blissfully unaware of the peculiar circumstances of the whole meeting. William stood back and observed the scene, waiting for a chance to question their visitor a little more. He wanted to find out her intentions, get some idea of how she had ended up here. It was fast becoming a farcical mystery.

It was one of those days in North Somerset when the clouds kept obscuring the sun before moving on again, giving the effect of a light constantly turning on and off. When the clouds had moved on the sun was hot on the skin; when it was covered by the cloud you could feel the chill wind from the sea blowing up the valley.

Sarah admired Louisa's dress, asking about the material and pattern, hoping she might say how she came by it. But apart from agreeing that it was nice dress Louisa said nothing that threw any light on her origins or how she came to Flax Bourton.

William tried talking about food and asking her what was the nicest meal she had ever had, expecting her to maybe reveal a name or a place or something about her family. But all she said was that she liked simple food.

When the questions got a little more pointed she always seemed to look downwards, ignoring the questioner, almost as if she believed that if she didn't look at them they would go away. She was clearly a little uneasy with any conversations about her past, her family, parents or where she had been in her young life.

After a while it became a little too obvious that the party were trying to get information out of her and Louisa suddenly lay back in the hay and started singing like a child. Little Johnny thought this was very funny and threw himself backwards onto the hay and began singing tunelessly "la-la-la" himself. Louisa didn't look at him but she smiled and sang louder, happy to have a companion in her craziness.

A few moments later Sarah and Amy pulled Johnny up by his arms and the little group left Louisa and walked back to the cottage, none the wiser about the woman in the haystack.

Back at the cottage William took control. "We are going to have to do something about her. I'll check at Barrow Court, Ashton Court and maybe Belmont. They all have rich visitors from outside the area from time to time. Maybe she has wandered out alone. She is not right in the head that's for sure and she must have come from somewhere. She didn't just drop out of the sky. Someone will be looking for her. I'm heading into Bristol now and I'll ask around and see if anyone knows anything."

Sarah and Johnny went back across the road - both determined to tell everyone they met about their strange encounter with the beautiful woman in the haystack.

William got Jessie ready, brushing her down and checking her hooves. The faithful horse stood placidly as he picked up each of her legs in turn expertly between his legs and scraped them to get rid of some of the muck and stones. He put a nosebag of oats over her ears and she ate hungrily as he washed down her rear and combed her tail. After half an hour or so he was ready and Jessie was hitched up to the cart once again for the trip. William got the gun out of the box, loaded it and stowed it safely, but readily to hand, in its usual place. Amy ran out to give her man a kiss as he climbed up, clicked his tongue and Jessie set off at a steady pace out through the yard and into the road. Amy closed the gate behind them and watched them heading towards the city until they turned a bend and disappeared from view.

William headed down the valley towards Bristol with the intention of stopping off at the gatehouse of Ashton Court to enquire of the gatekeeper there if he knew of any visitors to the estate. After the village of Long Ashton there was an entrance to the estate house and the lands that surrounded the fine old house that Sir Jarrit Smith had acquired after marrying into the Smyth family at a very convenient time when there were only women left to inherit the vast wealth.

William knew an estate worker called Tom, who was always around by that gate doing something or other to keep everything in trim and as he approached, sure enough Tom was busy working on a wall that surrounded some of the deer and sheep pens that were owned by Sir Jarrit.

He pulled Jessie to a halt and jumped down to talk to the older man, politely discussing the stones and wall before getting to the real reason for his wanting a conversation.

"I'll tell you why I stopped Tom. There is a woman sleeping in one of my haystacks. She looks like a lady. Got lovely clothes. A real good looking lady. Quite young. I think she might not be quite right in the head and I wondered if you had heard anything about someone of that description being missing. Thought maybe she might be a visitor to Ashton Court?"

Tom blew out his cheeks and said he knew nothing of any gossip of that sort.

"There was a strange carriage went through late yesterday though," he said, "went like a bat out of hell through the village. I think it was four horses. A large black carriage kicking up dust and causing a right old fuss."

"I saw it!" exclaimed William. "I was up on Bedminster Down and I could see it from there. I wonder if that is how she got there. She certainly doesn't look as if she has walked far. Her skin is so pale and her feet and legs quite delicate. Her shoes are expensive and there is no way she has walked a great distance in them. I bet she was in that carriage."

The two men stood for a while speculating on where it might have come from and where it might have been going. Most carriages heading for Taunton and South would have taken the upper road that William had been on. It was more direct and established and better for distance travel. The road out through Ashton, Long Ashton and Flax Bourton rarely saw anything other than local horses. There might be the occasional travelling tinker or gypsy but people like Tom and William pretty well knew everyone that they usually saw travelling along that road, by whatever means.

Of course things had changed recently with the coal mines opening up. That had attracted some people from further afield to work on the coal or to trade with the colliers. It was a new industry that was creeping into the rural life that William had been brought up in.

He thanked Tom for his time and got back onto his cart to travel on. Part of him was a little annoyed that he hadn't seen any connection between the carriage hurrying through the valley and the sudden appearance of Louisa before.

As he rode through Ashton it was Jessie who was really negotiating the way through other horses and vehicles that filled the streets. Everything became busier and grimier around Ashton where the mining business seemed to expand every day and where what were once rural fields were now seemingly more town than country. It wasn't far to the Southern edge of the docks in Bristol and it was fairly obvious that the way things were going Ashton would soon become part of the sprawl of the city. By a familiar warehouse on the dockside William stopped and made Jessie comfortable and tied her to a rail before entering. The scent of lavender hit him straight away and it took him a few moments to get used to the darkness and the strong scent sending shooting pains into his sinuses.

He called out and eventually heard the familiar voice of John Weeks, who ran this little factory mixing lavender with starch for powdered wigs, calling back from the gloom.

"Is that you John?" called William in a comical voice. "Is this the wig powder emporium or is it the famous black hole of

Calcutta?" he shouted and heard laughter in the distance from both John and some of his fellow workers.

"It is all very well for you William Atkings, some of us work for our living. We can't just trot around on our horses all day admiring the scenery like you."

Both men laughed and eventually greeted each other in the darkness, shaking hands and making their way out of the back of the factory to the daylight, overlooking the river. The tide was out and the water level was low and boats and sails were all at angles along the quayside.

The notorious Bristol tide wasn't helping in these tough competitive times. Many ship owners now avoided the docks because it added so much to their costs to have to stow everything "ship shape and Bristol fashion" as they called it, so that things did not slide around and get damaged with the tidal surge that was over 25 feet from low tide to high tide on most days.

With the conflict in America meaning that trade was getting more difficult in that direction and the city still recovering from the Seven Years War, which had ended just three years before in 1763, a city built on international trade was finding things tough.

The two men sat down on the quayside on wooden benches and one of the women that worked for John Weeks brought them a drink so that they could have their business meeting in comfort. The war had taken its toll. Somerset had been asked to provide men for the militia, men like William and John. But they didn't want to fight in a war they knew nothing about and had learned to duck and dive and avoid the ballot. Those they knew who had eventually ended up in the militia had earned good money, but many from Bristol had simply marched to Barnstaple, slept with a few women, had a few drinks, and headed back. They were now causing problems around the city, masquerading as "war heroes" while criticising those with families and jobs who had stayed out of the conflict.

William was planning to go to the Hot Well today. He knew

that many of those who travelled in to Bristol with money and fancy carriages made their way there to enjoy the waters. Of course they all had powdered wigs and John Weeks, with his lavender powder, produced some of the finest around. John trusted William so whenever he was heading over that way William would pop in to collect packets to deliver and John would trust him to bring back the money, with William taking a little turn for himself of course for providing the transport.

John wasn't sure how much longer the trade was going to last. Younger people like himself and William would never wear a powdered wig - in fact they thought it looked quite old fashioned and faintly ridiculous.

At Hot Well there were often those they called "Big Wigs", some of the richest and most successful merchants who liked to demonstrate their success with bigger and more elaborate wigs than anyone else. Of course the bigger wigs required more powder, which they could afford and which they liked to put on in heaps just to demonstrate that they weren't worried about the cost. It was all ridiculous and foppish to William and John but they weren't going to knock it if they could make money out of it.

There had been talk that the Government might introduce a tax on hair powder but John and William were of the opinion that it was unlikely to happen as the rich rarely seemed to find good reason to tax anything that they enjoyed!

Quantities and prices were agreed between the two men on the dockside then they loaded up the powder onto the cart behind Jessie and William was off again. He would have to negotiate the streets of Bristol, cross one of the few bridges and down more crowded streets to get to the fine houses where the Hot Well bubbled up beside the River Avon.

He enjoyed negotiating the streets. It was surprising how many faces he knew as he passed through and how much he could tell you about those faces and what might be going on in the buildings that he passed. There was an air of menace in some streets, yet a few hundred yards further and you could feel that everyone was relaxed and enjoying their day. There were poor people trying to scrape a living from doing anything they could in some parts of the city and then there were also rich people, riding in splendour with servants around them or bustling about on some official business. That was what he liked so much about Bristol, there was always so much happening and the sights and sounds and smells of the place inspired him and made him glad to be alive. He liked being busy, he liked wheeling and dealing, but most of all he simply liked being with people and seeing their funny ways.

It took him a full hour to get through the city and be heading out towards Clifton along the other side of the docks towards the Hot Well. There were two now that had been discovered. Really, he thought, they should be named Tepid Wells because the milky white bubbling water that came out of the ground close to the River Avon was only just warm.

Influential and fashionable preacher John Wesley had been ill when he first started drinking from the New Well and had made a full recovery. That had made the chattering classes from as far afield as London want to try this latest spa. In truth William felt the whole thing was a bit of a five-minute wonder. The wells didn't yield much water, it wasn't hot like that in Bath, the buildings of the spa were not as grand as other spas and the curative properties of the water were questionable to say the least.

But he was willing to make a little money out of fleecing the people with more money than sense that came along with their fancy ways to enjoy the "spa". You could basically charge them whatever you wanted and they would pay if they thought that it was fashionable. The middle-aged men from out of town, with their floozies in tow, loved it specially as they could persuade everyone to parade around naked and enjoy looking at the bodies. The great excitement then led to some liaisons in the evenings in the gardens around the area.

William's contact at the spa was Maggie Harrison, a very obliging lady of Irish origin who had found herself in Bristol after catching a Packet from Belfast with the intention of making a new life in America. But troubles at sea meant it put into Bristol and she had to spend some time in the city. She liked Bristol, didn't like the idea of more sea sickness and stayed longer than she intended. Then the war broke out and it just seemed safer and easier to stay in this beautiful little place pandering to the rich in the spa than to go anywhere else. Maggie was a character that everyone liked, with her Emerald Isle humour and ability to see the funny side of most things. William enjoyed chatting to her as she liked to make funny remarks about the worst excesses of those who attended the Hot Well.

Maggie was just inside the courtyard when William pulled up and came out grinning at him. He unloaded the starch, and she held a little in her hand and sniffed at the lavender, making a little purring sound of approval.

"Lovely," she said. "You will smell fresh all day after delivering that," and, cackling, she went inside returning with the spa purser, who paid William, wrote everything down in a book and then got him to sign. He carefully put the letters "WA" at the bottom of the page of script, not having a clue what any of the words said but trusting his regular customer to have logged it all properly.

As the purser went inside to find someone to help with the unloading, William turned to Maggie, "You haven't lost an aristocratic young lady from here have you? There is one sleeping in my haystack out at Flax. She is wearing the sort of "get-ups" the women here often wander about in. There was a carriage with a lot of horses that went past just before she appeared - it had come from this way."

Maggie replied, "Not that I'm aware of. Most of the women here seem to be rather quick to dispense with their clothes at the moment!"

William laughed. "Well, that may make her one of yours then. When I went to see her last night she was naked to the waist. A very fine sight it was too!"

"Oh William, I bet you enjoyed that! You would have laughed yesterday. One of the men here was naked except for a belt, on which he had two watches - one on Bristol time and one on London time. No trousers, no shirt, but he has to know the time in London! You couldn't make it up!" she said.

"Let me just ask inside for you, but I haven't heard anything at all. It's unlikely really that anyone would end up somewhere on their own - they travel everywhere in little groups for fear of the footpads and ruffians like you! Dr Read is in at the moment. He has been treating a few people here and prescribing. He knows most of what is going on."

Maggie asked William to wait in the little reception area while she went inside to see Dr Edward Read. He was one of the medical doctors that tended to the sick who came to the spa for cures.

He had studied and learned under Dr William Cadogan at the Infirmary in Bristol, an eminent doctor who had gone to London just over ten years before when he was elected a Governor of the Foundling Hospital. The two men had kept in touch and with Cadogan now a Fellow of the Royal College of Physicians, Read enjoyed travelling to London and mixing with some of the country's most eminent medical men and other famous people that Cadogan mixed with.

Read himself earned money from many sources. He was in great demand at St Peter's Hospital in the centre of the city, a private house that was now used to look after the mad, the sick and the poor. He had also taken up some of the controversial methods that Cadogan had suggested in his 1771 dissertation on gout, in which he said that lifestyle was the main cause of the illness. This earned him a tidy sum from some of the wealthier people of society in both Bristol and London.

Although many in the medical world had criticised the theory there were many fashionable people who took to the idea of temperance, careful eating and exercise as the secret of long life. Read soon realised that the richer, chattering classes would pay him good money for a diet sheet, some regular instruction and some exercises. Coupled with a glass or two from the natural spring and a few health-giving remedies, he found the spa a source of easy money, with most people not having a lot wrong with them. It kept him comfortably away from the hacking coughs, puss-filled boils, infectious wounds and dreadful plagues that marked his days at St Peter's Hospital.

William sat himself down in a big leather chair in the reception area while Maggie entered the book-lined office of Dr Edward Read, who was at his desk writing out some diet sheets for a small group from London that were spending a week at the spa. He looked up and smiled at the agreeable Irish lady, who made the days go by rather pleasantly here in the Hot Well with her constant flow of drinks and occasional cake and cheerful quips.

"Yes Maggie, what can I do for you?" he asked, smiling. She told him that a man who delivered regularly to the spa was sat outside and had been asking if any ladies were missing as one had slept the night in his haystack just outside of Bristol. Dr Read looked concerned and told her to show the man in. He stood as the man entered with Maggie and started to stare absent-mindedly at the shelves of books in the office.

William took off his hat as he entered the doctor's office but he was confident of talking to such an important man. Maggie listened in as the doctor turned and looked at him.

"I understand from Maggie that you have someone living in your haystack. Could you describe her to me?"

William hesitated, choosing his words. "I'd say from her dress she is a lady, from a fine and well-off family. She has long dark hair, very pretty. Quite young. I'd say around Twenty." He blew out his cheeks and thought some more.

"She turned up yesterday afternoon asking for some milk. My wife gave some to her and later we found her sat in the haystack. She stayed there all night. I'd say more than pretty… quite beautiful. A very fine lady. She has a strong accent…maybe foreign."

The doctor looked troubled. He asked hastily, "Has she told you who she is? Has she said anything about what country she comes from?"

"Not really," said William. "She has just said that her name is Louisa. That's about all. She seems like a bit of a dumbledoodle to me."

"A dumbledoodle?" said Dr Read.

"Yeah, you know. She's not got all her faculties about her. I'd say she has either had a bang on the head or maybe she was born like it. She's only a few steps from the madhouse, I would say. But she comes from money, that's for sure. You don't get clothes like that or skin like hers working on the land or living in poverty that is for sure."

"Fine. You are absolutely sure she hasn't told anyone who she is? Did anyone see her arrive? Did she get out of a carriage?"

William looked suspiciously at the doctor. There was something about the way the doctor was questioning him that made him think Dr Read knew something about the stranger. He seemed too anxious to ensure that nobody had been told her background. William chose his words carefully.

"Nobody saw her alight, but people say a carriage pulled by a number of horses passed along the road just before she knocked on the door of my home. I can only assume she got out of a carriage that had come from this direction - from Bristol. There is no way she had walked far in the shoes she was wearing. She asked for milk from my wife and thanked her profusely. She seems to get on with women."

"Has she spoken any languages to you?" said Dr Read. "I

mean other than English?"

"No Sir. If she did I wouldn't know it anyway. She has been singing a little song with nonsense words but I'm not sure if it is a language. She seems to understand the things my wife and I have said to her, but she doesn't always say much herself, like maybe she doesn't know all the English words. I'd say she is foreign but my wife wondered if she might be from another part of the country…we hear a few strange accents these days." He looked across at Maggie, who smiled and giggled. Her Irish accent was always a source of amusement between them.

The doctor caught the look between them and got the joke. "Indeed," he said. His expression changed quickly though and he sat behind his desk for a moment and put his hands to his forehead, seemingly deep in thought.

"How far are you from Bristol? Is this beyond Ashton Court?" he asked.

"Yes Sir, just beyond on the road out towards the coast. If you know that road it is beyond Long Ashton and you soon reach the village of Flax Bourton. That is where she was when I left this morning. She is showing no signs of leaving and I'd like to trace a relative or do the best for her if I could. She doesn't seem to know where she is headed. I'm not even sure she knows where she has been."

The doctor pondered. He looked a little agitated, picked up a pen and started writing.

"Look, I have some experience as a Mad Doctor and have treated lunatics at St Peter's. If this woman is a vagrant then I can bring her into care here in Bristol. But I shall have to come out and assess her. It is important that you do not ask her anything about her past. Don't believe anything she tells you. Questioning her may only make her more distressed and her behaviour more odd. She could turn violent, so do tell your wife to be careful approaching her."

William nodded at the advice, but didn't altogether believe it.

The doctor asked for his address and instructions on how to reach his cottage and the haystack and wrote it all down carefully as William spoke. He said it would be a few days before he could get there but if possible William was to keep the woman comfortable in the haystack and wait for his visit when he could make his expert assessment. Then with a nod of his head the doctor dismissed the pair of them and they walked outside together.

Maggie walked with William to Jessie, who lifted her head as they came near. The cart had been relieved of its load. Jessie seemed to know they were about to move off again and seemed restless to be on her way.

"That's pretty good for him. He's not usually that helpful and rarely goes anywhere unless he can make money - a typical doctor," said Maggie.

"I think it is for the best though. You don't want to have to look after that woman for too long." She patted Jessie on the nose as William silently made preparations around the cart. Then climbing up into the seat, he finally concluded, "I suppose you are right. It has to be sorted sooner, rather than later, and I suppose a doctor will know what to do. I just feel at the moment that I've betrayed her a little."

With that he made a clicking noise with his mouth and Jessie smoothly moved off and the cart turned back towards the Hotwells Road heading into Bristol. Maggie stood for a moment watching then went back into the spa.

Doctor Read got out his ink and pen and finest paper and started writing. It was a letter. He wanted to get it off straight away and he thought carefully as he wrote. Dipping the nib into ink and blotting as he went, he wrote elegantly and slowly. First his own name and the address of the Hot Well. Then the name of the person he so desperately wanted to tell about his recent conversation with William Atkings.

The letter read:

"Grand Master Thomas Dunckerley, Bristol Lodge.

My Dear Grand Master. I write in haste to inform thee that I believe I have located the young lady, who was discussed at some length last night, and who was passed into the care of the Lodge from the Premier Grand Lodge of England. I felt as thy humble Master Craftsman that I should get word to thee as soon as possible.

A well-meaning peasant visited me today and informs me that a woman matching the description is in the Flax Bourton area - this is a village but a few miles from Bristol. I shall attempt to detain her in the forthcoming days, using my powers as a health specialist and will ascertain if she has spoken of her origins to any of the locals here. I shall seek you at the Lodge meeting at the end of the week to inform you of my findings.
Your humble brother servant,

Dr Edwd Read"

He folded the letter carefully after the ink had fully dried and placed it in an envelope. He placed some wax over the flap of the envelope and took out a small seal from a desk drawer. Applying it to the wax, it formed a mark of an arch from a building. He wrote the envelope carefully: "For Provincial Grand Master Only, Bristol Lodge, College Green" then called to Maggie.

"Maggie, can you get a boy to deliver this right away into Bristol as soon as possible please, it is about some vital medicines." He took a coin from his pocket and gave it to her.

Maggie hurried to him and took the envelope. She went outside as the doctor went back into his study. Maggie wandered down the street towards Hotwells. She was looking for one of the boys that might run the errand into Bristol, but then caught sight of William Atkings' cart stopped outside one of the small stores that sold household goods. He had travelled just a few hundred yards on his journey from the entrance to the spa. She ran across the rutted track just as William came out of a shop with some candles.

"Hey William! Are you going past College Green? The doctor has a letter to be delivered there. Here is the money for taking it," she said handing him the letter and the coin.

He looked at the spidery writing on the envelope. "Where does it have to go?" he enquired.

"It says Bristol Lodge, College Green. Do you know where that is?"

"I do indeed. That's the Freemason place. There are some pretty powerful folk get in there from London. That's no problem. I shall be passing there. Hey look, let's split the money." He smiled and tossed a coin back at Maggie, who seemed delighted with the deal and waved him off as he hopped on board again and set off through the grime and the smell and the busy streets of Bristol, as sailors mixed with farmers on the quaysides and in the streets.

It didn't take long before Jessie was pulling the cart up the small incline to College Green, an expanse of grass in front of the daunting gothic stonework of Bristol Cathedral that was pretty much the centre of Bristol. One of the grand houses overlooking the Green bore a small wooden sign reading "Bristol Lodge". Next to the sign was a fairly anonymous door with a metal knocker. After stopping Jessie outside William rapped on the door and instead of it being opened, a small sliding hatch opened at eye level and the man behind looked out.

"What do you want?" the man inside asked and William held up the envelope so he could see it.

"OK, just pass it through," said the door-keeper and as soon as the envelope had disappeared through the hole the hatch was snapped shut again. William rolled his eyes and went back to Jessie.

"Come on. Time to head home old girl," he said to his horse as they set off through the crowded streets of the city.

Inside the Bristol Lodge the envelope was quickly taken along the corridor to a room where four men were busy chatting and smoking and discussing cargoes that were due to leave Bristol on the High Tide that weekend.

Thomas Dunckerley sat in the middle. At 41 years of age he was at the height of his powers and his time in Bristol resting and recovering had not been wasted. As a sea-faring Naval man he found the merchants of this city most agreeable.

He had been in Bristol for almost two months and the ministrations of Dr Read had helped him recover from the worst of the scurvy symptoms. Puffing on his clay pipe he could still feel the gaps in his teeth where he had lost them as the worst of the scurvy had hit him while he was in Marseilles.

Opposite him sat his son, also called Thomas, now 19 and at last a man making his own way in the world. He was pleased that Thomas had taken the time to travel to Bristol to visit his father. Young Thomas had already been on some voyages with his father and been introduced to some influential Navy people and now his father was keen that he should also get to know some of the influential people of Bristol.

Young Thomas was continually lighting his pipe trying to keep it going and enjoying the privilege of being his father's son. These last two months his father had further progressed the cause of freemasonry which played such a huge part in his father's life.

Decisions had been made that would see this city of Bristol have one of the most powerful positions in Freemasonry. Thomas Dunckerley had requested that the Province of Bristol should be formed. In anticipation of the formation many were already calling him Provincial Grand Master, a title he already held in other areas of the country.

Also sitting discussing the logistics of cargoes that needed to be loaded at the weekend were Thomas Dunckerley's good friend Captain John Ruthven. It had been Ruthven that had dropped him off at Marseilles to receive the treatment he needed when the scurvy took its hold from his ship, the Guadeloupe. It had been Ruthven that had picked him up on the Guadeloupe and brought him here for more treatment on the road to recovery from Dr Read at the Hot Well.

The fourth person in the room was Bristol Merchant Hugh Hayward. It was his cargoes that were being discussed. He was most anxious to know how they would be protected with the war in America and news of so much turbulence and privateering across Europe. He knew that the influence of Dunckerley and the experience of Captain Ruthven could help him to maximise returns. He was happy to be sharing a pipe of tobacco with them and enthusiastic about the way they were joining with so many other influential people to make the seas safer and ensure good profits from trading. Hayward was, or course, a Mason and fully aware of the great influence that Dunckerley had in so many areas.

One of the Tylers brought the envelope into the little room. The men stopped talking briefly as he handed it to Dunckerley, who recognised the doctor's handwriting from the envelope. He often sent little notes about treatments, so he placed it to one side.

"A note from Dr Read," he said to the others, smiling, "no doubt telling me how much fruit I must eat this week!"

"Ah yes," said Hayward, "but it seems to be working. You seem much stronger now. How are the legs?"

Dunckerley stretched out his legs and rubbed the back of his calf, replying, "Much, much better. I can't tell you just how painful it all was when I was in Marseille. You didn't see the worst of it, Hugh, by any means. By the time I got here it was really more just a weakness and the doctor has done great things with the help of the healing water at the Hot Well to get me back to this. It's only now as my strength is returning that I realise just how weak I was and what a toll the scurvy took on me."

Captain Ruthven nodded. "I've seen stronger men than you succumb to the scurvy. You are lucky to have found a good doctor. Now, are we all pretty much agreed that we will take all of the hogsheads to Welsh Back and then divide them from there? I'm pretty sure that is going to be easiest for loading and I can arrange it with some of the men at the dock, if that is what we all want."

The men nodded, Ruthven had made a good argument for the Bristol dock arrangements and none in the room knew more about loading ships in Bristol - or for that matter any other port - than the Captain.

With the decisions made and the discussions over, the few papers on the table were gathered up and the men began to chat more idly.

Ruthven turned to Dunckerley. "You know, I think all you have been through in the past six or seven years probably took more of a toll on you than you are willing to admit Thomas. You need to get that petition to the King finished. That will provide you with the finances to do all you can in freemasonry and everything else. There are so many influential people willing to back you up. The Duke of Beaufort was quite clear last night that he will support you."

Dunckerley and his son nodded and, as Hayward gathered up the last of his papers and put them into his thin leather case, the other three men extinguished their pipes and all were making moves to go. Hayward was ready first and bade everyone good day as he left. It was then that Dunckerley picked up the envelope from the doctor and, breaking the seal, took out the parchment inside and began to read. As he read the note his face changed and he sat back down, calling to his son and Captain Ruthven.

"I think we have a little issue to sort here. Edward Read has some intelligence as to where our esteemed lady may be hiding. He says he is going to attempt to detain her in the next few days. It's all getting a little out of control. We made promises to the Emperor and now it seems it is impossible for us to fulfil them. What good is a secret society helping the most influential and important people in the world if we can't control one young woman? The royal family in France have been asking questions and I fear that the whole secret will be out unless we sort things."

Ruthven and young Thomas looked concerned.

"How has the doctor got involved?" asked young Thomas. "How does he know about her and where she might be?"

Dunckerley looked annoyed and put his hands to his head. It was time for a little confession. Here he was, one of the most influential people in a secret society, the person who wrote the rules and who spent so long telling others how important it was to be careful about levels of knowledge and who would know what, and he had blabbed a little too much to the good doctor.

"I'm afraid I told him a little about her," said Dunckerley, then seeing their look of shock mitigated his confession. "I didn't tell him who she was. I just said that there was an aristocratic young woman that we were missing in the area and that we had been looking for her. We were discussing beautiful women and...well....you know...one thing led to another and I told him we were supposed to be receiving a beauty here in Bristol but somehow she had disappeared."

Ruthven nodded but young Thomas was a little shocked at his father's uncharacteristic lapse of judgement.

"But the doctor is relatively new to the Craft and is not on the sort of level where you can share with him this kind of information Father. You, of all people, know that."

"Yes, yes," said Dunckerley, "I suppose I have come to know Edward Read as a friend these last few months. He has really helped me get over the scurvy. His medications. Long days at the spa taking the waters and his programme of exercises to bring strength back to my limbs. I'm not sure without the fruit diet he put me on, the waters from the Bristol Hot Well and his attendance on me that I would even be here discussing this.

"Over the weeks we have talked about all sorts of things. Women especially. We were laughing and joking about the

Bluestocking ladies and their desire for books. Some society beauties came to the spa and we were playing a little game we were amusing ourselves with, just saying "cock" or "book" depending on which we thought each woman would prefer. He is a great laugh. All that led on to me mentioning the girl. I said I had been checking all the faces that came in to the spa in case she came in on the arm of a beau."

Ruthven put an arm on his shoulder. The long wigs of the two men lay lank between them as they looked at each other. These men had been through many things together and knew the world wasn't quite as straight-forward and perfect as it seemed to Dunckerley's young son. They also knew that staying calm and focussed in any difficulty usually gave them time and advantage. They were concerned at the situation but they knew that things could, and probably would, work out.

Dunckerley passed the letter to Ruthven, who started reading it for himself. After a moment the Captain folded the letter.

"I could get a party of sailors together to go to Flax Bourton and see what the gossip is in the village. They may be able to find her and bring her back. We would soon know whether the story is out," he said.

"No, I think they would be too visible in these villages. It is more likely to cause curiosity and draw attention to the situation. Let's just see what Dr Read finds. It may be a false trail. I want to spend time tomorrow on the petition to the King. It is important to me…" he looked at his son. "No, it is important to my family and Thomas here that the King acknowledges our presence."

Captain Ruthven accepted his friend's assessment of the situation. He had known Dunckerley in those dark days six years ago after his mother had died, when young Thomas was just a lad barely understanding the anguish that his father was going through.

He knew that the war in Quebec had been tough for Dunckerley. On board HMS Vanguard he had formed a Masonic

Lodge and had taught mathematics, all the time going over in his mind the amazing revelation that a neighbour had told him at his mother's funeral.

He had been with Dunckerley after the siege of Louisbourg, when as Captain of HMS Guadeloupe he had been the one to tell him that King George II was dead, and he had seen how the news affected him much more than others on board. He was with him in France months later when he resolved to tell everyone the secret of his birth and damn the consequences. He had taken him safely to Marseilles in the days when sometimes it seemed he would never recover from the scurvy and where he weakened and it seemed that maybe he would go to his own grave with the secret.

Now he was with him again here, in Bristol, and he had witnessed how the strength had returned to the man. How telling people the secret had emboldened him, made him stronger, made him respected. He knew how important it was for the circumstances of Thomas Dunckerley's birth to be recognised at the highest level.

Thomas Dunckerley now told everyone that he was the illegitimate son of King George II. Somehow the moment he learned the fact from his mother's friend, Mrs Ann Pinkey, he knew it was his destiny.

Ann Pinkey was a trusted neighbour who had sat by his mother's bedside in her final days and hours. During that time his mother had confessed to her that Thomas was the result of a liaison with the then Prince of Wales.

He had always felt he was something special. He always felt that there was something he had that others did not have. To finally find out that he had been conceived while his father was away and his mother spent some time at Lady Ranelagh's where the future king was visiting, had somehow explained everything.

It all made sense. His mother had told him herself that before her marriage the Prince of Wales and her - humble Mary Bolnest

- had been friends, close friends. But to hear the truth just after her death had caused him many, many hours of consternation. If only she had been brave enough to tell him herself in life. It explained so much. In his grief he had resolved to approach the King, his true father, but then, while he was away at war, the King had died. Now he was determined to explain the truth to King William III - after all, they were half brothers

It had been a difficult few years coming to terms with all this. But, amazingly, he found that the more he explained to people his position, the more he was accepted at the highest levels of society. Few could deny he looked like the King, few could question his leadership ability - surely a product of being from Royal stock.

Royal secrets were the best secrets. Secrets that could change a career. Dunckerley and his son - Thomas Bolnest Dunckerley - were really Royal Princes, and as such related to the best families in Europe. Only in the last year, as he recovered from the scurvy, had he come to realise that the secret his mother had passed on was not something that should cause him to be troubled. It was something of which he should be proud and which he had a duty to ensure would be of benefit to him.

His recent connections across Europe were moving him in the right direction - and with the aid of his Lodge brothers he now felt that all the cards were stacked in his favour. Tomorrow he would write the petition. Dr Read would find the girl. All the plans would be back on track.

Chapter Three

Love Song

THERE WERE TEN women sat around the haystack. Their voices were raised and from a distance you might think they were having a leisurely time just gossiping and being idle. But in fact every one of them was busy at some task as they talked. Some were darning clothes, two were preparing vegetables in large buckets, one was knitting and others were drawing out yarn. Louisa sat in amongst them, helping by pulling on bits of cloth and supporting shanks of yarn. A stranger might at first think she was one of a close-knit group, but would only have to observe them for a short while to realise that Louisa was the odd one out.

Firstly, of course, there was her exquisite figure and beauty. Somehow even the best looking of the other women just didn't seem to have the shape and grace of her neck and her movement.

Then there was her clothing. Everything that Louisa wore was of the finest cloth, silk or was highly decorated. Today she had tied her hair up high to tower above her finely-boned face. It was a style the country women of North Somerset had hardly seen but two had taken off their cloth hats and allowed Louisa to show them how she did it - much to the approval and humour of the others.

Then there was the chatter. The soft Somerset burr, littered with slang words and phrases came thick and fast from the women, except Louisa, who seemed to struggle to catch some of the phrases. Every time she joined in the conversation it slowed in pace as the Flax Bourton ladies tried to explain what they had said or make out what Louisa was saying.

Amy was enjoying the afternoon. She was preparing shallots in large amounts so that they could be stored to last through the winter. There was always an abundance of certain vegetables in certain months of the year and the key thing was to ensure that it lasted through the thinner days of the year when the ground around her home was rock hard and yielded little that you could eat for months.

It was good to have the other women from the village there, along with her friend Sarah Derrick. She knew that every one of them was testing out the stranger, trying to get to the bottom of how she had ended up here in Flax Bourton. It was a great distraction and a novelty for them. Having such an exotic stranger joining in with them had made the day go faster and had prompted stimulating and interesting conversation.

But, although they had probably been chatting and laughing and working together here for over an hour, Amy felt no wiser about where Louisa had come from and had been given little clue as to where Louisa intended to go. Sometimes she seemed sophisticated and knowledgeable, especially when it came to fashions and clothing. Yet, she clearly knew how to do domestic chores and at times she seemed to be lacking in simple manners or acceptable behaviour. Amy had concluded that Louisa was quite likeable. She was fun to have around. She wasn't the brightest person she had met and sometimes seemed to fall into depression or sadness but then a few moments later would be wildly singing or laughing almost hysterically.

The women often sang as they worked and it was Sarah Derrick who, tiring of the constant quizzing of the stranger, chose a gap in the conversation to shout, "Come on ladies, let's have a sing-song!"

Then without waiting for any response and without any accompaniment she sang out sweetly and clearly:

"Abroad as I was walking one morning in the spring.

I heard a maid in Bedlam so sweetly she did sing"

It was a song they all knew and as soon as that second line was over all the women, except Louisa, joined in heartily:

"Her chains she rattled in her hands, and always so sang she

I love my love because I know he first loved me.

"My love he was sent from me by friends that were unkind:
They sent him far beyond the seas all to torment my mind.
Although I've suffered for his sake contented will I be,
For I love my love because I know he first loved me."

Louisa was listening intently trying to make out the words of the simple folk song, smiling at the women around her and joyous at the way they carried on working, with the rhythm of the song somehow signalling to their hands how they should work as they peeled, and darned and sewed.

"My love he'll not come near me to hear the moan I make,
And neither would he petty me if my poor heart should break;
But though I've suffered for his sake, contented will I be.
For I love my love because I know he first loved me."

Sarah Derrick stood up and with a wave of her hand silenced the others so she could sing the first two lines of the final verse on her own, bringing huge guffaws as she over-acted and made fun of the words:

"I said: "My dearest Johnny are you my love or no?"
He said: "My dearest Nancy, I've proved your overthrow."

The women whooped and sang the last two lines with gusto:

"But though you've suffered for my sake, contented will we be
For I love my love because I know my love loves me."

Louisa stood and applauded and laughed and did a little dance. The sheer joy and fun of the women all singing together made her so happy and she was still bouncing up and down and clapping when all the other women had finished laughing.

"I think that one could be a candidate for Bedlam herself," said Sarah Derrick quietly to Amy and although the two women smiled and giggled they both knew there was a degree of truth in it. Louisa didn't seem entirely stable. After all, what woman would want to spend her days in a haystack chatting to complete strangers? None they knew. Given the fact that her clothes and her demeanour seemed to indicate her background was from a higher social class, it seemed even more crazy.

John Chapman was the first of the men to appear. He walked towards the group and smiled at his wife Susanna, who finished off the stitches she was on, stuck the needle and thread into the cloth so she could resume it easily, and picked up her things. John was slightly embarrassed and intimidated by being the focus of the women and kept his distance. But he couldn't help but stare at Louisa, who was still standing and dancing to the little tune the women had so recently stopped singing. Susanna caught the look and glared at him. He looked at his boots and Susanna ran over to him, took him by the arm and they wandered off to their cottage nearby. John's appearance signalled to the women that it would soon be time for all the men to return from the fields and from their work and they would want to be fed when they got home.

Amy looked back towards her cottage, wondering if William was back yet. She and Sarah Derrick decided they should take their leave together. Louisa was still dancing and singing. "For I love my love because I know my love loves me" was sounding more West Country almost every time she uttered the line. Amy touched her arm and pulled her to one side, making her stop her singing and listen.

"We are going now. Is there anything you need for this evening? Why don't you come up to the house with me? Have a little bite to eat?"

Louisa looked at her. "Trouble and misery dwell in houses," she said and with that started dancing around again and singing.

Amy and Sarah shrugged and laughed at each other and started the slow plod across the field towards their cottages. It seemed the village visitor, who had been two nights in the haystack, would be there for a while yet. In truth it was a novelty and word had certainly spread as, during the day, women had arrived from Farleigh and from Downside, a few miles away, to look at the stranger in the haystack and draw their own conclusions.

The two friends separated at the cottages and went inside to go about their usual routines. It was a full 30 minutes later that Amy heard William's cart pull up outside and he walked in with Willie Wilmot at his side.

Willie took off his cap as he entered the cottage and put down the small leather pouch he had in his hand on the table. It was a familiar event for Amy. The arrival of Willie usually meant a little boost to the finances as he had sold some goods and would be sharing the profits out with her husband. She didn't interfere with their business but instead reached down the bottle of gin and without asking poured them each a tot and put it down next to them.

Willie had done well. The trinkets he had taken during the meeting in Barrow Gurney had all been bought by a dealer in Bath at the best prices and the men divided their money and sealed the deal by clinking their drinking mugs together and taking a sip. Satisfied his work was done, William turned to his business associate. "Come on. I'll take you to see the maid in the haystack. You can see what all the fuss is about."

Then turning to Amy he said, "I met a doctor in Bristol and they are coming out in the next few days to take a look at her. Willie here thinks she might be a gypsy."

"Yes, I've been told she is wearing some fine clothes but apparently there was a gypsy camp out near Satlford village on the way to Bath a few days ago," said Willie. "They had a tent and charged people to go into a show. I believe they were from Europe and it was some sort of dance troupe or entertainment troupe of travellers.

"All the men wore colourful britches and buckled shoes with fine embroidery and the women also wore fancy costumes for their dancing and the like. I think that is who you have here in the haystack.

"When I went to Bath some of the locals said there was a hell of a row among the gypsies. It seems one of the dancers was carrying on with the husband of one of the others. They were last seen heading into Bristol and the person I spoke to said she feared for the life of the young girl that had committed the adultery. They don't mess around in those gypsy groups."

The two men walked across the field. The other women had left but Louisa was dancing by the haystack alone as the two men approached, lifting her skirt a little and doing some obviously well-rehearsed routine. She hadn't spotted the men as she was absorbed in her own little world.

"There you go - trust yer old friend Joseph Wilmot. Without a doubt she is a gypsy dancer. I tell thee that dust cloud you saw heading south past here would have been the gypsy troupe. They had a number of carts and coaches and horses that they rode in displays. They were master horsemen and well able to drive them at that speed.

"I'll warrant this is the girl cast out by them for her sins and still in her dancing clobber. She's no lady, she's a stinking gyppo, probably from one of those foreign places. That's why she can't understand you properly."

William saw Louisa slightly differently now. It did make logical sense. The aristocracy looked after their own and surely nobody of noble breeding would be cast out in such a way to have to spend time in a haystack. Her clothes were unusual but now he looked at them they were definitely of foreign design and so striking and colourful that maybe they were made more for show than for practical wear.

The two men walked closer and Louisa saw them and smiled at William. She plonked herself down in the haystack as they approached.

"Good evening Louisa," said William. "This is my friend Joe Wilmot. I was telling him about you. He's a good friend."

"Nice to meet you ma'am," said Willie Wilmot, once again taking off his cap in the presence of a woman. Louisa looked slightly bashful and fiddled a little with arranging her skirts.

"That was some good dancing you were doing there. Where did you learn it?" asked Willie, trying to sound like it was a casual enquiry.

"I have always danced. I danced when I was a child. Dancing is good," said Louisa, smiling.

"It is. Do you dance to the fiddle?" said Willie, miming a violin with his arms.

"I just enjoy dancing," Louisa answered.

"So you are a performer then? A traveller? You perform in a group of dancers, is that right?" Willie casually sat on the side of the haystack, not invading Louisa's space but feeling they were now chatting seemingly as friends and inwardly rather pleased at the progress he was making at solving the mystery.

"I don't understand," said Louisa, turning her head away.

"You dance for money? You dance in a group? With other women?" Willie asked, warming to his theme.

"No. Not me. I just dance today because I am happy," said Louisa. "I like it here. The people are very friendly. We have had fun today singing."

Willie Wilmot looked at William Atkings significantly and nodded as if he was about to deliver the killer question.

"Go on, sing us one of your traditional songs. We'd like to hear it."

"Oh I only remember a little," said Louisa.

"That's fine with us. Let's hear it. We love to hear traditional music from around the place. As you say, we are friendly folks around here."

"Right," said Louisa clearing her throat. There were seconds of anticipation as the men waited, expecting to hear a folk song in a native language, the sort that the travelling troupes might perform as they passed through.

Louisa bellowed out in a broad West Country accent:
"But though you've suffered for my sake, contented will we be
For I love my love because I know my love loves me."

The two men burst into laughter and Louisa stopped in her tracks before joining in their merriment.

William Atkings slapped his friend on the back. "She sounds like she comes from as far afield as Cheddar, me babby," he shouted as tears of laughter began to form in his eyes. Pleased with the reaction Louisa belted it out again:

"But though you've suffered for my sake, contented will we be
For I love my love because I know my love loves me."

Her slightly mangled version of the tune she had heard earlier that day made the already laughing men laugh some more and that only encouraged Louisa to sing more. The more she sang the two lines of the chorus the more the two men found themselves in uncontrollable fits. Amy had made her way across the field to find out where they were and saw the men laughing and when she realised what it was about joined in as well. She broke up the little party by handing over some bread and other food she had brought out for Louisa and signalling to William that it was time he made his way back for his own supper.

They soon stood at the door of the cottage saying their goodbyes to Willie Wilmot.

Amy said, "I think you might be on to something there Willie. She may well be from travelling stock. Earlier today she made a strange comment to me about not wanting to live in a house. Said something about there being trouble and misery in houses, I would imagine that's the sort of attitude you might get from a gypsy traveller. They don't much like settling down and its probably what she was taught by her parents. I guess the doctors will know best so we can wait until then. She isn't doing any harm there - everyone seems to get on with her. If the poor wretch has been thrown out by her kind then she doesn't have much of a future."

"That's true," said Willie. His horse was tethered just outside the cottage and he took it and climbed up on board, bidding his goodbyes to William and Amy as he headed back to his own home for his supper.

Around half an hour after Willie Wilmot disappeared there was another visitor to the cottage. A man from the nearby hamlet of Farleigh stood at their door with maybe a dozen or more eels hanging down the front of his chest and all strung together on string that was around his neck.

He had been fishing in the drainage rhynes that criss-crossed the fields nearby for half the day and was travelling door to door trying to find buyers for the fresh water eels he had caught. William used some of the coins he had received from Willie to buy two of the fat eels and then proceeded to gut them and clean them before presenting them to Amy for her to cook for their supper.

The eels were a treat for the pair, who loved the fresh earthiness they offered and Amy was careful to make a bowl up for Louisa and keep it warm by the fire as they ate theirs together. After they had finished they took the dish to Louisa who ate it hungrily, perched in the haystack. The couple once again attempted to find out some information from her but she simply ignored them and smiled at them and thanked them. As soon as she was finished with the food, she settled down in the haystack and Mr and Mrs Atkings walked back to their cottage hand in hand.

The next morning William awoke to hear the familiar hiss of fine rain falling on the tiles of the cottage just outside his window. The sky seemed to be pretty much on the floor and it was a dank and grey world that he entered as he made his way to the closet for his morning ablutions.

The rain fell steadily, straight down. It soaked the leaves of the tree branches overhanging the toilet area. Once he was back at the house William and Amy exchanged glances over breakfast and both knew the other was thinking of Louisa out in the elements.

"What are we going to do about her?" said William.

Amy looked a little forlorn. She had no answer. She liked Louisa and the afternoon sat with the other women in her company had been one of the most interesting and fun she had spent for a long time. But she knew that something had to be done. She pondered for a while.

"She doesn't really help herself much," she said eventually. "I've tried to persuade her to perhaps come indoors where maybe we can sort her out with some normal clothes and get her into normality but she won't have it. She's either very clever or very simple. She never answers anybody's questions about where she is from. But she is such fun and...well...basically I think she is harmless."

"Yeah, I suppose," said William. "Hopefully the doctor will be able to come up with a bit of advice. I don't mind her sitting there but...well...it's just not normal is it? I worry about her out there. Anything could happen. Look at the weather!"

They both stared out of the window at the constant teeming rain and in their minds were speculating on what it must be like at the haystack. They knew they would soon have to go out to see her. Unspoken between them was the obvious thought that any sensible human being would seek shelter in such weather - yet there was no sign of Louisa knocking at their door and asking to come in out of the constant downpour which, judging by the clouds, was likely to continue for the rest of the day.

After they had eaten Amy packed up some food and a drink and started to put on her head shawl to cover her from the worst of the elements. The Atkings' had two old cloaks made of a stiff material that they used on wet days and they got them from their pegs and put them on before venturing across the field. Louisa was crouched at the bottom of the haystack sheltering from the worst of the rain as they arrived and looked surprisingly cosy. Amy passed over the food and asked her if she would like to come into the house to eat it but she refused. She seemed quite happy and after few moments the couple felt it was pointless standing there getting wet so they hastily made their way back to their home and shook the cloaks out and hung them to dry in the porch close to Jessie's stable area.

William got the coins out that he had received from Willie Wilmot and started arranging them into piles. Among the coinage were two Louis D'Ors. French money. Often people paid with Louis D'ors but values had been fluctuating wildly recently with the wars and he wasn't sure whether his best tactic was to move the coins on quickly or hold on to them. He looked carefully at the coins and the flowing locks of Louis XV. He had heard how France was now ruled by his grandson Louis XVI from the lavish palace of Versailles and stories of decadence and of the beauty of his young wife Marie Antoinette had fascinated him. Although he had travelled little William was always intrigued by stories of other lands and would always buy another drink in a pub in order to sit through a traveller's tales and listen to a story from someone from abroad.

The rain showed no sign of abating and he decided that today he would work on some of the jobs he had been saving up for just such a day inside the cottage. He had no real need to travel. Stashing the majority of the coins in a bag he noticed a silver coin of unusual design and picked it up.

The "head" had another flowing-locked monarch from Europe on it. Around the edge was the word Franciscus - he knew that to be Emperor Francis I, Emperor of the Holy Roman Empire until his death a while ago. The date on the back said 1756 - ten years ago. This was another royal he had heard a lot about. People had said he was a philanderer with many women lovers years younger than himself. The coin was in good condition - very little wear and the picture of him quite detailed.

He looked at the profile with its distinctive nose and laughed, calling out to Amy.

"Look at this. Who does it remind you of?" Amy took the coin and moved it in her hand to catch the light. It was such a dull day she could hardly make out the coin so she took it over to the table once again where the light from the window fell on it.

"Oh yes. I see it! Louisa!" she said. "But this is a man isn't it?"

"Yes, it's the Hapsburg emperor - you know the one who died last year. I think he's father of Marie Antoinette. He could pass as Louisa's brother!"

The pair giggled and William threw the coin into the bag with the rest of the money, then put it in his "secret place" to ensure that the proceeds from his work did not get stolen. There were few crimes in the community but being on a main road there was always the risk of vagabonds passing through entering houses for whatever pickings they could find.

Two hours later the couple were working together in the kitchen of the small cottage. William had lit a fire in the grate and a whiff of blue smoke curled from the chimney and mingled with the rain that still fell steadily on the roof and clattered down the pipes into the water butts and other items that were gathered outside to catch it.

On wet days like this the whole village seemed to look in on itself and although the city of Bristol was just a few miles down the road it might as well have been a hundred miles away. Little had changed in the last 100 years or so in the village. It was a simple rural life that the Atkings' enjoyed.

Yet somehow they knew changes were coming. There was so much talk of America and Canada. Many people in the city had travelled the world. Fabulous stories of the royal family in France; the changes across Europe; and the exotic stories of Africa, where slaves were being rounded up, were common in the pubs and cottages now. The world was getting smaller.

The local gentry earned much of their money from the "triangular trade" taking items to trade in Africa for black slaves then shipping them across to the New World to sell and bringing back from there all the luxuries of modern life - tobacco, sugar and cotton. It was coming over in such large quantities that new jobs were starting just processing the new goods.

The day passed quickly and soon William and Amy were lighting the candles in the small cottage as the rain continued to fall steadily outside and the cloud cover brought early darkness.

"Can't have been much fun out in that haystack all day today. We have to find a way to get her to live somewhere indoors. How long do you think she is going to stay there?" said Amy.

"Well she's quite a catch for a man so I don't think it will be long before someone takes her under their wing," said William. Amy made a face.

"What about William Turner up at Belmont? He's still single," said William jokingly.

Amy giggled at the reference to the local scandal. "He must be over 50 by now. Yes, perhaps she is young enough for him!"

The pair sat contemplating the stories that had unfolded over the last few years about Turner and which had provided many an evening of merriment and gossip among the local people - especially over a gin or an ale. William Turner was a rich land owner with a fine house on the hill overlooking Flax Bourton.

Eyebrows were raised when he proposed to Hannah More, a woman 20 years his junior and now well known for her poetry, teaching and campaigning. He was completely smitten with her and she helped him create a beautiful garden at Belmont House as he spent much of the money he had earned as a successful merchant.

But years went by and there was still no sign of a ceremony and then gossip spread that they had broken off their engagement. Hannah More, who had made enemies among some of the influential men of Bristol and Somerset with her strident views against men, was mocked heavily. Most women also found it amusing that she had insisted that they should demand more independence from men and get themselves educated. Her sisters ran a school in the middle of Bristol but her rather strident and modern viewpoint didn't convince too many people in the rural areas. She seemed well-meaning enough but her failure to marry the man whose proposal she had accepted seemed pretty bad form.

William certainly thought it was her unwomanly ways and strident campaigning that had put off Turner and led to the two lovers splitting up. Turner was embarrassed by the scandal and it was said he gave Hannah More a yearly allowance now to enable her to be independent. She had gone to London a lot over the last few years and was said to be getting involved with actors and musicians, artists and other famous folk.

William broke the silence. "I hear Hannah More is hardly in Bristol these days. She was last seen with her sisters months ago holding some kind of protest outside the Mayor's parlour. I think she still goes up to Belmont when she is down this way and they have some fancy friends down from London - maybe Louisa was there for something and wandered out. It's nearer than Ashton Court.

"I could check it out. Turner is a strange one. Quite what has gone on between him and Hannah More I don't know. These days he seems to hang around with that friend of his called Joe. There are rumours about them flying around. In some ways I can't say I blame him for not going through with the wedding. She's not one that a man is ever likely to be able to control."

Amy answered, "That's for sure. I can't see her obeying any man, even if she loves and honours him so marriage is out for her. He's so much older than her too. I don't know what she saw in a man of that age anyway. He was twice her age."

"It's surprising how many women are more attracted by money than looks," said William, "It's not like you falling for me because of my handsome features and strong body." William looked significantly over at his wife and she smiled.

She took off her apron and walked over to where he sat. She sat on the floor in front of him and ran her hands over his thighs looking up at him with big eyes. She knew the effect it would have on him.

"Well, I don't think women like Miss Hannah More really know what they are missing," she said. "It seems a lot of people these days put more store in reading books than living their real lives."

William reached down with two hands and lifted her head towards his face and they kissed passionately. William stood and grabbed his wife by the arm, pausing only to lift a candle with the other hand, and he took her quickly to their bed.

The rain lashed against the window and the evening wind picked up and blew notes through the tiles and gaps in the eaves of the cottage.

Outside Jessie shifted and snorted in her stable. The horse picked up her rear right leg and rested it with the hoof on its "toe". She started to doze off standing there with that one leg relaxed as the wind and rain buffeted the outside of the stable.

Across the field stood the haystack with the rain dripping through the gaps in the hay. Louisa lay on the sheltered side of the stack in a cosy straw "cave" she had made with the cloth coverings the Atkings' had provided, making a rudimentary shelter from the worst excesses of the storm.

She felt calm. Almost serene. It was a comfortable place. It was a safe place. The people seemed kind. She had seen so many things over the years that she had learned to appreciate moments like this. Certainly she was comfortable with her own company. She knew storms did not last forever. Rain was always followed by sunshine.

She reached into her bag and pulled out a small purse. Inside she looked at the gold coins. Alongside was a small colourful piece of cloth. A handkerchief. She removed it and placed it by her nose. If she concentrated hard she could just about still smell the perfume. After enjoying the trace of sweet scent for a moment she put the cloth back inside the purse. The rest of the bag was made up of clothes. Fine clothes, some underwear and three linen caps. She took the cap with a blue ribbon running around it that was used to keep it in place on her head. She pulled it over her hair, secured it in place then settled back into the hay. It was time for sleep.

The misty miserable rain continued throughout the night and at dawn the green hills had disappeared and just seemed to be hidden by a flat grey sky. Louisa had now been in the haystack for three nights.

Word about her had spread around the district and speculation was growing. The Atkings' were also beginning to wonder what would happen when they needed the hay that was providing shelter. They needed it for Jessie, they needed it for a whole range of things in their lives. The whole village had gathered together at haymaking and shared the harvest between them.

Theories were now abounding about who the stranger might be. There were fanciful tales that she might be a foreign princess cast out of her palace in some kind of coup; maybe as Willie Wilmot said she was a gypsy whose behaviour meant she was cast out from her traveling tribe; some took her strange behaviour as madness and suggested she had just wandered off from somewhere not knowing what she was doing or maybe she was a victim of the modern pirates - kidnapped on the High Seas and brought to Bristol on a ship from which she had escaped.

The thoughts were going through William's head as he awoke still curled around the body of his wife. He could still smell the scent of last night's sex on her and pushed his hard body against her for a few seconds before climbing out of bed ready to face the day. He knew he would have to go into Barrow Gurney today despite the weather. Cripple Cock was due back from Taunton today and William was keen to learn how much he had achieved for the house clearance items he'd taken.

The thought reminded him and as he stretched by the side of the bed he reached out and got hold of the little bell, tinkling it until Amy began to shake her head at the noise and start to move.

She rolled over on to her back and her breasts spread out flat. William took in the view and tinkled the bell again.

"Come on woman. A man needs his breakfast!" Amy opened one eye and looked at him and smiled.

"That bloody bell. Is it morning already? I just want to stay here."

William grabbed at her breast and she jumped and leapt out of bed. As she went across the room he slapped her rump and she howled and laughed at the same time. Amy pulled on some clothes and went to the fireplace and began setting the fire for the day, only pausing briefly to look out of the window at the grey miserable misty rain that slashed across the fields, hung in the trees and covered the yard with puddles. The path to the latrine was muddy and rain spattered so she pulled on her boots before leaving the house.

On her way back she glanced towards the haystack. From here the only sign that Louisa was there was a white piece of material hanging out in the rain on part of the haystack. It was probably one of her blouses. Amy thought about going down to the haystack but decided it was too early, there was too much to do and anyway she had little to say to her. As she trooped back to he house she thought some more about the circumstances. Back in the kitchen the fire was starting to take hold and William had put a pot on.

"You know, it's a bit annoying that she can't even come up here to see us," said Amy, "when you think about it we are the mugs waiting on her hand and foot. She doesn't even come up to get water. I deliver it to her. I give her a pot to piss in. Take all her food. It would be good if in return she came up once in a while and offered to help out with something. She could come and make the fire up or something."

"Yeah, you are right," said William. "Its a bloody cheek really. Perhaps we shouldn't have shown her so much kindness. I think she is definitely taking advantage of you a bit. Don't worry though, we'll get it sorted soon. There must be somebody who knows her. Probably some family that will come and collect her or something. It's all a bit weird but we will miss her when she is gone."

Chapter Four

The Hospital

DOCTOR EDWARD READ sat alone in the ornate boardroom of St Peter's Hospital reading the notes that had been left for him about the Patten family from St Stephen's Parish. Mr and Mrs Patten and their three-year-old son were just one room away waiting to see the eminent man and hopefully get a solution to their problem. The boy was not normal. The notes said his features were those of a Mongol and his odd behaviour sometimes frightened his parents. In the last few months he had become powerfully strong and Mrs Patten found it hard to discipline him. They feared he was becoming a monster. They had raised six other children and none had been like this. They couldn't cope with this extra burden on their lives.

Edward Read pored over the notes. Sitting beneath the colourful mural of "Daniel in the Lion's Den" beneath the gold-embossed ceiling, behind the massive oak desk with its carved legs, he felt the power of his position. Of course all of this decor had been commissioned by the wealthy former owner of the building, Robert Aldworth, when it had been his magnificent residence as one of the city's Merchant Venturers and before it fell into public use.

The hospital was a rambling building with bits added at different parts of its history. The Pattens were waiting in a dull room with multi-paned windows streaked with rain that looked out over the small gardens that led down to the river. The authorities knew how to use the contrasts in the different parts of the building to good effect.

When the Pattens were led out of their room by a shaven-headed hospital orderly through a dingy corridor to the bright, large ornately-decorated room where Dr Read was sat they would know their place. They would have no doubt who held the power here. Three chairs had been placed in front of the desk and even the young boy seemed in awe of the ceilings, the bright colours of the murals and gold on the plasterwork, to such an extent that he sat quietly next to his parents. His mother instinctively put her hand across him to hold him in position. She knew this stillness wouldn't be for long and his condition would manifest itself by his misbehaviour within minutes.

The orderly, who was a big man, stood behind them with his arms folded, near the door through which they had entered.

Dr Read greeted them with a smile and then said rather formally, "Just to confirm you are Mr and Mrs Patten and this is your son of three years, Joseph? Am I right?"

"Yes, you are Sir" said Mr Patten. Joseph started squirming in his seat and his mother pressed her arm tighter across him.

"Good. I have read the papers. I understand you wish him to be committed here if possible. Is that right?"

"Yes Sir. We have six normal children and we just can't cope with him. He is powerfully strong as you can see Sir. I think it be best if he lives here at the Mint Workhouse. Best for him and best for us your honour," said Mr Patten, adding an unnecessary and exaggerated address to the learned doctor, who smiled and rather enjoyed the reverence that the couple were giving him.

"Let me look at him," said the doctor, getting up from behind his desk and walking towards the boy. He grabbed the boy's arms but Joseph struggled and Dr Read nodded towards the orderly who came over and also grabbed the boy's arms pulling them backwards. The boy might be powerful but, at three-years-old, was no match for the giant who had grabbed him and was soon looking straight at the doctor.

"Yes, we see a number of these. These features are a sign of Mongolism and you are quite right he is likely to become very strong and difficult."

The doctor took the boy's hand and checked the trademark single crease across the palm. He had little doubt. But just for good measure, and to impress, he said to Mrs Patten, "Did the boy have white spots in his eyes when a baby?"

Mrs Patten's mouth fell open. "Yes," she said with surprise. "Yes, he did. I noticed that. I'd never seen that before."

"I thought as much," said Read, walking back to his desk. "There is no doubt. We can take him in here at St Peter's Hospital - what you folk call the Mint Workhouse - but you will have to pay some of the cost of his keep until he is able to earn some money through labour in a few years."

"Really? said Mr Patten sounding shocked. "I thought in this sort of case he could be looked after here and maybe trained up for something."

"Look," Mr Patten, "this is delicate but I'm sure you understand that you must take responsibility for your actions in bringing him into the world. We have some charitable funds from generous merchants but it doesn't cover everything. We do what we can. The committee would decide the level of your contribution and they will take into account your earnings. It will be no more than the cost of having the boy at home and you will not have to cope with the problems that you have now."

"We earn very little. I don't think we can afford much," said Mrs Patten.

The doctor's mood changed instantly. He sat behind his desk and looked at the couple.

"Do you drink Mr Patten?" he asked.

"Me?" asked Mr Patten looking confused.

"Yes, Mr Patten - gin - do you drink gin?" the doctor asked forcefully.

Mrs Patten glared at her husband as he looked confused. He knew he had to answer his superior's question but he didn't have the wit to know what the right answer might be.

"I have imbibed occasionally, your honour," he said.

"And Mrs Patten do you drink - gin?"

"I have Sir, but in modest quantities. Neither of us have the funds to drink gin a lot," she said. Her sentence tailed off as

Joseph, unable to move as he was pinned by the man holding him, began to cry and mumble, "mum, mum, mum" trying to reach out towards her.

"Have the pair of you engaged in sexual intercourse after having gin?"

The couple looked at each other and looked embarrassed at such a personal question being aimed at them and neither wanted to answer. The doctor filled the silence.

"You see, that is probably what has caused the affliction with Joseph here. I would say almost without doubt that he was conceived when either one of you or both of you had been drinking gin and the seed was passed in an inebriated state within your bodies - poisoning his brain. The other possibility is that you, Mr Patten, had a venereal disease at the time of conception - that is when you two had sex resulting in this offspring. Did you sleep with a poxy woman around the same time as you slept with your wife?" the doctor asked matter-of-factly.

The couple looked shocked and ashamed and Mrs Patten looked accusingly at her husband as the boy struggled and screamed.

The doctor continued as the shocked couple stared ahead, "We can take the boy. We can take him today. But you must agree to contribute. After all he is the consequences of your actions. Do you understand?"

The pair nodded and at a signal from Dr Read the assistant lifted Joseph and carried him away from his parents as he screamed and shouted "mum, mum, mum". Mrs Patten burst into tears, emotions welling up in her as her son so quickly vanished from the room and her husband sat shame-faced next to her. She glared at him again and he tried a little smile back.

"Go back outside and I'll prepare the paperwork for you to sign before you leave," said the doctor, leaping from behind his desk. He shook their hands as the devastated couple trooped back out through the door. He barely noticed their reaction as he wanted to prepare this paperwork quickly and get moving in the hospital carriage out towards this village of Flax Bourton. He wanted to see this woman and hopefully please Thomas Dunckerley. Dunckerley could help him to progress in so many powerful places with his connections in London and Europe.

Read filled out the consent forms. He knew there was little likelihood that the Pattens could read but someone on the staff of the hospital would read it to them and get their mark. The hospital was tucked away down a narrow lane behind St Peter's Church. Parts of the building dated back to the 14th century when it had been the grand home of a merchant.

It had been in the last century that the part of the building he was sitting in now had been built and the coat of arms of the Merchant Venturers was on the fireplace in the room he occupied for the assessments and admissions. This was a regular task he carried out with his medical qualifications helping him to assess those who would be admitted to the hospital because of their mental illness.

Of course many needed little assessment. Their mad behaviour was usually the thing that had brought them to the attention of the hospital. Part of the building that housed the maddest and most difficult people had been used by Bristol Corporation as a mint at the end of the last century when the buildings fell out of private ownership and became used for civic purposes. That was why just about everyone in the city still called it the Mint Workhouse from its first name when the Corporation of the Poor in Bristol set it up.

Doctor Read felt proud that in these enlightened times the Bristol Poor were looked after in this way. In this one building there were areas that provided sanctuary and sometimes work for those who otherwise might be sleeping rough on the streets; there was a madhouse for those whose brains were affected by birth defects, accidents or some other malady. There was also a medical facility and infirmary for those who had physical injuries.

The Bristol Corporation of the Poor paid him a reasonable sum for his duties and with his work at Hotwells Spa and his private practice he was comfortably well off and able to hold his own with the other merchants. Joining the freemasons had also helped him to mix with the right people - many of which became sources of income as they consulted him for their ailments and problems.

The orderly came back through the door and the doctor passed him the paperwork to go to the Pattens and asked him if he could be ready in half an hour with the carriage. With that he pulled on his coat before exiting into the wet narrow streets of Bristol. Up the hill and around the corner he went into the coffee house. Up the narrow wooden steps to his usual spot where he sat with his coffee and had a smoke, watching the citizens of Bristol scurrying by just below the window. It was a filthy, wet horrible day and the prospect of a carriage ride out into the country to see a woman sat in a wet haystack didn't fill him with a great deal of joy.

Coffee cup drained, he paid and retraced his steps to find two large shaven-headed hospital orderlies already sat patiently waiting inside the carriage with its horses harnessed up and ready for him. Seeing the doctor approaching they leapt out and, putting on their cloaks, climbed up into the front to drive. One asked the doctor if he knew exactly where in Flax Bourton they were heading. Dr Read said he wasn't sure but to look out for hay ricks and once at the village they would ask. He gave the men the toll money for Bristol Bridge and, opening the door for himself, climbed up inside the carriage.

Through the city he leaned on the window, idly watching the people outside. Once the coach was bumping along the country lanes on the edge of the city he pulled the curtain across and settled back. He was dozing when the carriage came to a halt in Flax Bourton.

The light through the side of the curtains told him it was still raining. He could hear the men asking people and one replied,

"Oh you mean the Maid of the Haystack. I'm not surprised she's attracting some attention from the wealthy, she is a beautiful woman, who any man would like to be near."

Read smiled. He didn't think of himself as aristocracy. But I suppose to these simple rural people he must seem fabulously wealthy. He would say he was "comfortable" financially. His studies to be a doctor had placed him in a good position and his wealth was building. Of course, this fine carriage was not his own. It contained all the hospital needed for collecting and transporting lunatics with ease.

He pulled back the curtain and saw the basic rural cottages of Flax Bourton looking dull and miserable in the rain. The carriage was moving at walking pace and one of the assistants was walking alongside trying to locate a house they had been told about. Within a few moments the carriage was stopped outside the home of William and Amy Atkings and the doctor shook off his tiredness from his sleep, stretched and opened the small door so that he could climb down into the muddy road.

Amy was inside alone when the knock came on the door. William had set off for Barrow Gurney to meet up with Cripple Cock and had promised to be back within a few hours. But she knew that he was likely to stay for a drink or two if the goods had raised good funds in Taunton.

She opened the door to see the doctor in his fine wig and clothes standing in the rain flanked by two large bald-headed men, who looked more than capable of looking after themselves.

"Good afternoon Madam. I am Dr Edward Read. I have come from St Peter's Hospital in Bristol as I believe you may have a vagrant lady that has taken up residence in a haystack. Your husband spoke to me."

"Oh, come in doctor," said Amy. "Yes, you are in the right place. What a filthy day. Do come in out of the rain. My husband is due home very soon and he is best placed to deal with this. The woman is called Louisa, she is in a haystack in a field at the back of the house."

Doctor Read and the orderlies were more than happy to get out of the rain but once they were inside the small cottage they seemed to take up most of the modest little room. Dr Read refused a welcome drink and said he had a few questions and he and Amy sat opposite each other around the kitchen table as the two huge orderlies stood like giant bookends next to the fire, warming themselves after the journey.

"Your husband says she has been behaving oddly, but that from her dress and appearance she may come from a wealthy background. Is that correct?"

"I'd say so. Her dresses are so fine and her hands and face and neck are not like a working woman. Sometimes she can be delightful but other times she can be very odd. To be honest I quite liked her when she first arrived but now I don't know what to do. We can't keep feeding her and looking after her. She won't come indoors and she just sits there in the haystack."

Dr Read thought for a moment, then said that he needed to question Louisa personally and that it would be helpful if Amy would come with him to introduce him to her. He looked meaningfully at Amy.

"From all I have heard she is showing every sign of being a lunatic. She may have been perfectly friendly so far but as you may know lunatics are affected by the phases of the moon. There is a possibility that during that four week cycle she could turn violent and you and other people in the area may be in danger as a result. She could cause harm to children, for instance."

Amy looked concerned but quickly replied, "She has shown no sign of violence or anger during the days she has been there. She is sometimes insolent and won't look at you when you talk to her. She doesn't tell you anything about her past or how she got here or what her plans are. She is odd, without a doubt, but not violent."

"Believe me," said the doctor, "lunatics can change so quickly.

One day they are perfectly calm and friendly, the next day they can be murderous and evil. The moon is a powerful thing."

At that moment William pulled into the back yard with Jessie and after a few moments putting the horse into his stable he came into the room and greeted Dr Read, thanking him for coming out to the village on such a miserable day.

The doctor repeated his theory to William, who nodded and a few minutes later Amy and William led the doctor down towards the haystack. The rain was a little lighter but still falling. The two orderlies followed a distance behind and as they got to within 20 yards of the haystack the doctor signalled for them to hold back and they each squatted on some old wooden crates that were stacked near a hedge as the doctor and the Atkings' walked around the haystack to confront Louisa.

She looked pathetic and pitiful curled up in the haystack trying to keep as dry as possible under the grey miserable sky. The floral pot was outside the haystack full of piss and rain. Rain was dripping through the hay and limp pieces of soaking wet material that had been tied around the haystack hung forlornly over her head.

She was wearing a mop cap that was wet at the back and the shoulders of her dress were a darker shade of red than the rest where the rain had dripped onto it, so that it was now soaking. She looked more miserable and disturbed than Amy and William had ever noticed before and they saw a look of shock on the doctor's face as he caught sight of her for the first time.

"Louisa," called Amy, "I've brought someone to see you. Dr Read has come out from Bristol to meet you."

Louisa turned and smiled. Her dark eyes met those of the doctor and even in her dishevelled state he could appreciate her beauty. The doctor crouched down so that his face was on a level with Louisa's as a gust of wind blew another blast of rain into her face.

"Hello Louisa. It is terribly wet this morning. I need to talk to you. Shall we go inside for a little?"

Louisa averted her gaze and simply stared at the grass around the haystack. If she ignored the doctor maybe he would go away. But, firmer now, the doctor repeated the question.

Louisa looked up at him. "It is nice here. Nothing good can happen in houses. You find happiness and liberty in fresh air."

Doctor Read was slightly taken aback. Clearly Louisa was educated by the way that she was speaking but her stubbornness and refusal to go inside while the rain soaked into her was not logical or the behaviour of any sensible person. He spoke to her again.

"Where have you come from? Where were you living before you came to the haystack?"

Louisa looked away and down at the floor again, her face now a little tense. It was clear that she had heard the question perfectly well but had no desire to help the doctor with an answer.

William felt the awkwardness in the air and thought he might help by talking to Louisa. He told her the doctor had come all the way out from Bristol, that he was here to help her and that he needed just a little information to maybe get her back to her family and friends.

Louisa looked at William and Amy, just a hint of a tear coming to her eye. "I am happy here. This is a good place."

The non co-operation of Louisa and the relentless rain seemed to slightly irritate the doctor and he rose from his haunches and set off towards the two orderlies without a word to William, Amy or Louisa. The married couple followed on after a few seconds and the little group once again piled inside the little cottage.

Doctor Read looked resigned and sat down on one of the hard chairs by the kitchen table. He seemed pensive and lost in thought for a moment, then turned to William and Amy.

"Clearly this lady has a foreign accent. Has she ever mentioned that she might be from Germany?" he asked, "only it seems to me that might be her origin. She is also showing signs of lunacy and I think the best course of action might be to take her to St Peter's Hospital where we can examine her more easily and decide how she can best be of use to society."

William answered, "A few people have said she is foreign. She certainly isn't from around here. How she came to be here is a complete mystery. We can't keep looking after her so the hospital may well be the best place for her. She has very few possessions. All in a little bag she arrived with."

The doctor signalled to the two orderlies who left through the back door and started to walk across the fields towards the haystack. When they reached it Louisa was singing happily to herself and the sudden arrival of the two large men, both strangers to her, took her by complete surprise.

She hardly had time to gasp as one of the men picked her up and threw her slight frame over his shoulder, clamping his hand firmly on to her buttocks to hold her against him. She was hoisted into the air and was spinning wildly around as the other orderly grabbed her bag and gathered up the few clothes that were around and followed on as they started the slow tramp across the sodden field towards the road.

Louisa suddenly came to her senses and started to struggle. The orderly chuckled and thrust his hand between her thighs touching her in the most intimate place and causing her to open her mouth in a shocked gasp. The orderly following behind switched her bag to his left arm and reached up to grab her hair and push her down firmly on to his colleagues back. Every time she moved she could feel the thick fingers of the orderly between her thighs, so she soon decided her best tactic was to simply stay still and wait for her chance to escape.

William and Amy were still inside the cottage, dingy because of the cloud cover, discussing theories about how Louisa might have got to the haystack with the doctor, when one of the orderlies returned and said simply, "She is in the carriage".

Amy looked surprised. "She is happy to travel back with you?

We have hardly seen her move a few yards from the haystack since she has been here."

The doctor smiled. "We are experienced at dealing with maniacs and lunatics. You have to be firm. It is for the best and she will have a nice dry bed and food this evening. She can't stay here in all winds and weather and you haven't got the means to look after her, and why should you? She's not your responsibility. Well, I'll bid you good day as we had better get her back to Bristol now."

With that the doctor and the orderly left and Amy and William followed them to the door. The curtain was pulled on the carriage and the doctor entered by the far door. The orderly climbed up on the driving seat of the carriage alone and it set off, turning in the road after a few yards to make its way back towards Bristol.

The couple looked at each other, both slightly surprised at what had just happened. In a strange way they would miss the young woman who had been sitting in the haystack. But maybe it was for the best that she get the care and attention that she clearly needed in her condition.

The carriage rattled its way towards Bristol. With the orderly, the heavy coat of Dr Read, Louisa's bag and clothes and Louisa herself all crammed inside there was little room. The orderly sat in front of Louisa, his face just inches from her own and she spent most of the journey with her head turned, her eyes focussing down on the stones of the road, which was all that she could see in the small gap beneath the blind that was pulled.

No words passed between Dr Read and the orderly for the whole of the journey and soon it was clear, from the change of pace of the carriage and the different tone of the wheels on the road, that they had entered Bristol. The carriage pulled to a halt at the toll for Bristol Bridge and then a few moments later swung around a bend and pulled up outside the hospital.

The orderly stepped outside first and quite gently helped

Louisa down and she found herself in a small courtyard with the fine Tudor building that was the hospital looming over her. The orderly held Louisa's arm and led her up a few small steps, through a big oak door and into a large empty reception room. Louisa seemed calm, if slightly cowed, and the doctor signalled to the orderly that he would take over.

He sat behind a desk and pulled out some bits of paperwork and within a moment or two a matron came through the door and spoke in soft tones to the doctor before turning to Louisa.

"Now young lady. I believe your name is Louisa? Do you have any other name?"

Louisa looked at the floor, ignoring the woman. Her expression hardly changed. It was as if she could not even hear the matron.

"Can you give me your last permanent address?" Again, no reaction from Louisa, just an insolent downward casting of her eyes.

"Well, perhaps we can have a little chat tomorrow," said the matron. "We are going to get those wet clothes off you, get you cleaned up and find a nice comfortable bed for you. OK?"

No reply. The matron walked over and tried to pull Louisa by the arm towards a door but she was now rooted to the spot and resisting.

"I'll have to get the boys in," she said to the doctor, who was still busily scribbling at his desk and he just waved his hand dismissively. He knew the matron was experienced and trusted her to just get on with her job.

Matron left the room for a moment and came back in with the two orderlies who had travelled out to Flax Bourton. They had taken the carriage and horses to the stable boy and had removed their coats. Both were smiling and jolly as they came through the door and looked at each other with a degree of glee.

Without saying a word they grabbed Louisa under the arms on each side and propelled her through a doorway with matron following. It was such a slick and powerful movement by two big men that her small frail body was in no position to resist. Within seconds all four of them were in another room of the hospital, this one less decorated. In one corner there was a tin bath filled with water and just about the only other furniture were two chairs facing the bath and a small stand with a large cloth on it and a rough garment that was basically a long cotton dress.

Louisa started to struggle and one of the orderlies grabbed her arms from behind and pinned them back - her breasts thrust out in front of her and the other orderly started pawing at them, grabbing handfuls of them and twisting and starting to roughly pull her clothes over her shoulders. The matron stood by and started laughing.

"OK boys, that's enough," said the matron and the orderly in front of Louisa stood back. His colleague continued to hold her with her arms pinned behind her.

The matron went close to Louisa and spoke softly to her. "Come on dear, it will be better for you if you co-operate with me. We need to get you nice and clean and into bed so you can rest. I'll take your clothes and get those clean and back to you in a day or so. The faster we can do this the faster you can be safely tucked up in a nice bed."

Louisa's head slumped and the matron nodded at the orderly who loosened his grip and Louisa spoke for the first time, "Tell them they can go," she said. The matron again signalled to the two orderlies who backed out of the room, watching all the time in case Louisa suddenly changed her demeanour.

As soon as the men had left the room Louisa started to take off her clothes and put them on the chair, the matron smiling at her now. Once she was naked she climbed into the bath and matron took a jug and started to help her wash her hair.

"We will find you a nice room tonight. You'll soon settle. You have some fine clothes, where did you get them?" she asked casually.

"My father paid for them," said Louisa. "I've always had good things."

She felt the calming effect of the water and started to scrub at grubby feet and legs and picked up a small block of soap. After a few minutes the matron left her and went to retrieve towels from another room. When she returned Louisa was quietly singing to herself. She encouraged her to dry off and put on the garment that had been left for her.

The matron had also brought in the bag of Louisa's things and put it on the floor next to her as she was finally dressed, her hair still wet and tangled.

"Do you have a comb in here?" asked the matron, and Louisa nodded and searched through the bag to retrieve the comb.

"Come on," said the matron and Louisa, carrying her comb in one hand and the bag in the other, padded barefoot alongside her through a short corridor. She was placed in a small room, which contained a bed, a small writing desk and a chair. There was a multi-paned window overlooking a courtyard, the frame nailed shut tight so it couldn't be opened. It looked out towards the slow moving river, the glass covered in raindrops. Louisa sat on the bed and matron wished her goodnight and left the room.

Louisa sat combing her long dark hair for a few moments then climbed into the bed, an action which made her realise for the first time just how cold her feet had become. She settled down calmly and fell asleep for her first night in St Peter's Hospital.

- Chapter Five -

The Decision

THOMAS DUNCKERLEY HAD walked across College Green towards Bristol Cathedral. A weak sun was pouring light through the trees providing a fresh feeling after the morning rain had cleared. As he reached the High Cross he saw Captain Ruthven deep in conversation with two other men, one of whom he recognised from Lodge meetings, although he wasn't entirely sure of the gentleman's name.

As he approached they broke off and Ruthven shook the hands of the men and said his goodbyes and fell into step with his friend. They both started to stroll towards the coffee house just down from the Lord Mayor's Chapel. Dunckerley had the petition in a small leather case and as soon as they were settled at a table with their coffees he removed it and passed it over for Ruthven to read.

It was in the beautiful fine hand of Dunckerley and set out the circumstances of his birth as he understood it from Ann Pinkey. It gave lots of details, names, places and dates and as he read through it Ruthven felt quite dizzy, confused and it soon became a blur of details.

But the gist of the story was clear. Dunckerley was the illegitimate son of George II and as such should have some patronage from the current king. Ruthven put it to one side.

In reality he had skimmed through the final paragraphs but he turned to Dunckerley, who was sipping his coffee and looking out across College Green. "Yes, I think that is fine. I would expect many people to back you on that and the King certainly can't ignore such evidence."

Dunckerley nodded sagely and Ruthven looked at his noble features - he certainly resembled the King, that was clear, and also couldn't be denied. Many other influential people were now backing his petition and Ruthven felt it would certainly be good for him to be in such esteemed company.

Dunckerley showed him the section where he had left space for those supporting his claim to sign their names. He lifted a small ink pot from his bag and a nib and passed them to Ruthven who signed it with his full rank of Captain with a flourish, allowing the paper to dry before rolling it up and passing it back to his friend.

Indeed, among the crew on board ship Dunckerley was often already referred to as "His Highness" or "His Majesty" without a curl of a lip these days. Most believed his story and his demeanour certainly was that of a Royal figure.

"Thank you so much," said Dunckerley, "I shall not forget the wonderful support of my Masonic friends in this. You can not understand the grief and turmoil I have been through over the years, but I think at last we are close to getting the recognition.

"When I saw Emperor Francis and brought him into the Craft, he saw me as a fellow blue-blood and realised the importance of bastard children. That is why he passed the secret of his own illegitimate daughter to me for safe-keeping."

Captain Ruthven and Dunckerley sat in silence for a few moments occasionally sipping their coffees.

Ruthven pondered on the subject they had talked and talked and talked about in the last few months. What had started out as a lucrative favour for Emperor Francis of the Holy Roman Empire had now taken many twists and turns and was still not resolved. With the Emperor dead and most others with any knowledge of these matters trying to put it out of their minds Ruthven and Dunckerley had a Masonic secret that they truly needed to off-load.

Dunckerley had told his old friend Ruthven how he had found himself in a unique position with Francis, one of the most powerful men in Europe. As his sponsor and mentor in the Masons the Emperor looked up to him; indeed Dunckerley had helped to form a Masonic Lodge covering the Circle of Franconia. It was the heart of Germany and Dunckerley had set up Francis as its head.

So when he needed help to conceal and support an illegitimate daughter born as a result of an affair, it was to Dunckerley that he turned. Dunckerley could call upon the support of Masons throughout the continent.

It had all started for Dunckerley one night when he and Francis had been drinking following a Masonic ceremony and Francis had tears in his eyes as he listened to Dunckerley pour out his feelings of how he wished he could have spoken to his mother just once about his regal birth; how he had always felt there was something strange about his up-bringing and how appalling it was that someone born out of true love between a king and a person he loved so much ended up cast out while someone born to a king within a loveless marriage went on to rule a country and have all the power and influence. He told how the feelings had driven him to set his own rules, build his own power base with the Freemasons and live his life of independence.

Suddenly Francis was sobbing, telling him he was so right and telling him about his own affairs of the heart. He had been brought up with Maria Theresa. They had played together as children. She had always been a friend but maybe because of that there was little spark of sexuality, mystery or excitement between them. Others decided that she should be his wife for political reasons. She was an able queen and empress and although they ruled together he believed she was the better ruler, while he concentrated on financial matters.

They loved each other, he could not imagine life without her, after all she had always been there. But she never seemed to provide enough for him. There was something missing. He knew he wasn't the type to be monogamous. His status gave him so many opportunities as he travelled and even at their wedding he had hesitated three times before signing the marriage vows.

He didn't want to be a hypocrite and make all those promises he knew he couldn't keep.

He had told Dunckerley, "Thomas, I remember that day in 1736 as if it was yesterday. The quill pen was in my hand and I had to sign the book. Maria Theresa stood at my side looking beautiful - the sort of woman any man would want to spend the rest of his days with. But I laid that quill pen down, I couldn't sign because I knew I couldn't keep those promises. Maria Theresa told me not to be nervous, I picked it up again, I put it down."

"Can you imagine Thomas - a royal wedding. All of the courtiers, all of the officials, the religious leaders, the army leaders all stood around. I couldn't just say "I'm sorry I could never be faithful to one woman". Eventually I signed and the deed was done."

Maria Theresa loved him dearly and had borne him 16 children. But he had told Ruthven how much more exciting his times with the much younger Princess D'Auersperg had been, especially in the bedroom. The inevitable happened and the Princess became pregnant. Their daughter was born without anyone knowing about her. The secret child had been named Felicia Juliana and soon after birth was sent to an isolated community in Bohemia where she was brought up in a house by two women, one of which she called Mama. The other she knew as Catherine.

Francis had been touched by Dunckerley's story of his illegitimacy and realised his own daughter, Felicia, was in exactly the same predicament. She would be denied any recognition, and yet she had been born out of real love, while his other daughters would become wives of dukes and kings, and his sons emperors.

As Ruthven pondered once again on these tales it seemed Dunckerley was also thinking through the story as he suddenly spoke once again about Francis I the Holy Roman Emperor.

"You know Ruthven, since his death it has all got out of hand. I'm not even sure if the girl that came across to England is his daughter. Felicia was born the same year as her half-sister Marie Antoinette. Imagine that, Ruthven, one is now possibly the most famous and fashionable woman in the world and Queen of France, the other was supposedly coming into our care and we may have an imposter or things have been made so difficult for her that she has lost her mind."

"We were told by Lodge members in London that she was on her way to Portsmouth. Then I heard that she was being sent to see me here in Bristol. Now it seems she has disappeared and nobody is sure if she is here or elsewhere. I was told by one colleague who stopped by last week that she proved to be very difficult in London and that she has run away. I do not understand why she has run away."

"Many now believe the girl that came across to England is an imposter. If we reveal her as a princess and it is proved to be false then my own petition to the King will be weakened. We need to settle this matter. This girl has been passed through so many Lodges in recent months that I can't be sure it is her."

As the two men chatted a young lad came into the coffee shop and went up to the woman behind the counter. They exchanged a few words and he headed towards the table where Dunckerley and Ruthven were sat.

"Mr Dunckerley?" the boy asked, waving a a piece of paper that was folded and sealed. Dunckerley nodded, took the letter and gave the boy a coin for his trouble. He studied the seal before opening.

"It's from St Peter's Hospital, must be Dr Read". He opened up the note and told Ruthven its contents. It was a short note simply informing Dunckerley that the girl from the haystack was now safe at the hospital and asking him if he would like to come in to see if the girl was indeed the person that he was looking for.

"It's more important that I get this petition into the hands of the King. I'm not sure how I could recognise the girl for certain, I've never met her."

"This could be her; there could have been a terrible mix-up after she was questioned or this could be someone entirely different. I think we need to try to see her for ourselves but first we have to secure the seat for taking this message to London."

Ruthven nodded. The pair drained their cups and set off for Corn Street where they intended to ensure that Dunckerley's petition could be securely taken to London and the King through one of the regular coaches that left from that street.

They walked past the ships being loaded in the centre of the city, pausing to talk to some merchants they knew and to check out some barrels that were being unloaded. The cargo was similar in size to the one they had been discussing with Hayward and they discussed the relative merits of St Augustine's Reach or Welsh Back for loading as they climbed the incline into Corn Street.

The clock on the Corn Exchange had an extra minute hand showing the time in London as well as in Bristol. The men checked their own watches against it then took Dunckerley's carefully wrapped and sealed petition into the small booth where parcels and letters were collected, paid the carriage and walked around the corner and down the narrow street of half-timbered medieval buildings towards Bristol Bridge before taking a left turn and finding themselves at the imposing doors of St Peter's Hospital. The courtyard outside was busy, but mostly with waifs, strays and people of the lower orders and the two men were able to push past them and make their presence known to an orderly stood just inside the heavy oak doors. He beckoned them inside and after asking after their business ushered them into a side room to wait for Dr Read.

Read soon entered the room with the matron who was carrying a large bundle - all of the possessions retrieved from the haystack and the clothes that Louisa had been wearing. She put them down on a large wooden table and left the three men, who immediately started searching through the items.

Dunckerley spoke first. "Thank you so much for your efforts Dr Read. Is this everything that the girl had with her?"

"Yes," said Read. "The clothing is of a good quality, some of it the finest, and there were these few coins and trinkets but nothing of any major value."

"No portraits at all? It makes me believe that this is not our woman. I was assured that she had with her three portraits, one of a man and two of women. They were her most precious possessions and she is unlikely to allow herself to be separated from them."

Dunckerley and Ruthven examined the clothing and again Dunckerley shook his head.

He turned to the doctor. "The woman we are looking for would speak German well, and reasonable French. Thank you so much Dr Read for what you have done so far for us but I can't be certain that this is not our woman.

"We are looking for a girl called Felicia. She is of German origin. The person we are looking for was brought here to Bristol from Belgium by ship by Brothers in the Masonic Order. She went missing some days ago, as I told you."

Dr Read said, "She answers to the name of Louisa but she has given us very little information so far. She has an accent and could be German but she seems to understand English well."

"If I can prevail on you one more favour," said Dunckerley.

Read was delighted to be asked to get further involved and eagerly nodded his acceptance of whatever task the powerful Dunckerley asked of him.

"Perhaps you can question the girl and see if she slips up, gives you any clues, or indicates in any way that she might be our Felicia. She was brought up by a woman she knew as Mama and another called Catherine.

"Few people are aware of those facts. Question her and use your judgement as to whether those names mean anything to her."

"I would be delighted to Mr Dunckerley. She is sleeping now but later I will personally question her thoroughly and I'll report my findings. The information you have passed on is most useful. She is reasonably compliant at the moment, but shows some signs of madness, either obtained due to a head injury or through a brain defect, I can not be sure. From that point of view she does not communicate in a straight-forward manner. But we are used to these types of situations and we can certainly ensure that we get to the bottom of this little mystery and either rule the Maid of the Haystack in or out of your important equation."

Dunckerley and Ruthven pushed the bundle of clothes and trinkets back across the table and stood to go. They said their goodbyes to Read and Dunckerley leaned conspiratorially towards him and told him that his efforts would not be forgotten.

Dr Read beamed proudly as he showed the two men to the door before turning back in and ordering the matron back into the room to retrieve the bundles and take them back into the hospital stores.

A few hours later Dr Edward Read sat behind his desk at St Peter's Hospital as Louisa was led into the room by the matron. Her belongings were carried in by an orderly and placed on a table nearby where a clerk began meticulously writing down a description of each item she had. The clothing was certainly of a foreign design and manufacture. She had a number of gold and silver coins from various lands in a blue bag, a small model of a teapot that a pedlar might sell; a piece of cheese and a collection of mop caps and hats. Finally there was a silk scarf. Everything had been inside a large, good quality bag, that probably came from London.

While the inventory was going on Dr Read asked Louisa to take a seat. She sat on the chair rocking to and fro and wringing her hands in distress. Read looked her directly in the eye asked her straight questions.

"Where do you come from?"

"You brought me here from a haystack just outside the city," said Louisa, sounding far more confident than her demeanour suggested.

The doctor shook his head and smiled then asked again, "Yes, I am aware of that. I mean before the haystack; where did you live before? Where were you born?"

"I'm not sure Sir. I have travelled a lot. I don't remember, Sir."

"Do you have any family?"

"I don't believe so Sir. I believe my Mama is dead and I never really knew my father," said the girl.

"Your Mama is dead, you say. Did she bring you up alone?"

Louisa looked at the floor and seemed to be sad thinking about her mother.

"Was there someone called Catherine in your childhood?" asked Read, staring intently, looking for a reaction.

Louisa said nothing. She started to wring her hands and look distressed.

"Are you alone in the world?" asked the doctor.

Slowly Louisa lifted her head and looked at him.

"Yes Sir. I have been travelling. I am a travelling person."

"A gypsy"

"In a way Sir. I have travelled many miles. I prefer to be outside Sir. There is only bad things inside houses."

The doctor was experienced at people trying to avoid his questions. He didn't get the feeling with Louisa that she was being deliberately difficult. It seemed she genuinely had little idea where she had been or where she had come from. He stood up and went over to her and she sat passively as he explained he wanted to examine her head.

She had a fine head of hair and he pushed his fingers through it checking all around until he found evidence of an indentation and a scar from a serious wound that had now fully healed.

"I see you suffered a head injury in the past. How did you

get that?"

"I fell from a carriage Sir. I don't remember much about it. I was younger then. It was before I came to this country."

The doctor realised he had a little breakthrough: "Which country did you come from?"

The girl looked down and said nothing. The doctor persisted. "Which country do you originate from?"

"I was told my father came from Bohemia," said Louisa matter-of-factly but then she fell silent and would not speak or answer any other questions. She started rocking on her chair again and looking more and more distressed as the doctor questioned her.

"Do you know anyone called Felicia?" he asked, turning to watch her reaction.

Louisa looked as if she was genuinely concentrating for a few moments then slowly began to shake her head. "No….no I don't think I know anyone called this," she said. It seemed a genuine reaction to the doctor.

He looked at her again. "Sprichst du Deutsch?" he asked.

Louisa looked confused and looked down at the floor. He could not discern any recognition from her. He went to the door and signalled to the matron who was outside. She came in and the doctor addressed Louisa one last time. "I think you will need to stay here a few more days while we look into your background further. Do you have a last name?"

Louisa just stared at the ground and said finally, "I go now. There is no happiness in places like this. I need to go now."

Tears started to well in her eyes and the doctor nodded at the matron, who gently caught Louisa's elbow. She stood and allowed herself to be led away by the matron back to the room that she had been sleeping in.

Dr Read took the sheaf of papers written by the clerk detailing her possessions and her clothing and went to his office where he wrote up his notes. That evening he stuffed all the papers into his bag, grabbed his coat and set off to walk to the Freemasons Hall at College Green. He climbed the short hill before turning left past the medieval buildings then down through Corn Street where a few merchants were still doing business among kegs of ale and bags of corn. He crossed the wooden bridge over the River Frome and finally through the alleyways to the Lodge where his knock on the door was recognised and a tyler opened it immediately to let him inside.

Read found Dunckerley in his usual place, sitting with his son and Ruthven, pipes in mouths, studying some sea charts and chatting. The three men nodded as he entered and Dunckerley signalled for him to sit down on a vacant bench by the table.

Dunckerley spoke first. "Well, my good doctor, have you news of the girl."

Read took out the papers and laid them on the table. "Here is a list of all her belongings that we could find around the haystack. You saw most of them on your visit. I examined her briefly today and she says very little about her background. I examined her physically and she does have an old head injury which may have caused her to lose her memory and may explain some of her strange behaviour. I am not so sure that she is a lunatic. I believe she is more likely to be a maniac or possibly a simpleton, rendered thus by an injury, such as a fall from a horse. We see it quite a lot and it can take many forms."

Dunckerley's eye was running down the list of belongings; the fact that the clothing was foreign made and the descriptions of it made him believe this girl might well be Felicia daughter of Francis.

"Did she say anything about her background? How she came to be here?" Dunckerley asked.

"Very little," said Read, "although at one point she suggested her father came from Bohemia but after that she would not say another thing. She appeared not to recognise German or the name Catherine."

Dunckerley looked shocked. "She said her father came from Bohemia? Thanks for your work on this Dr Read, I will pay you for your time and trouble but I'm beginning to think, on balance, that this is not the woman that was brought to Bristol by the Masonic Order."

Dunckerly pulled open a drawer and sorted through some money. He agreed some fees with the doctor and gave him a small amount for the welfare of the girl, suggesting the doctor decide what was best to do with her.

Dr Read said, "I doubt we will get much more out of her. She is without doubt confused and says all sorts of things that may or may not be true and seems to have little realisation about the real world. If she says anything that makes me suspect in any way that she is the girl you are looking for then I will gladly pass her into your care as nobody else seems to be making any claim on her and she says she has no family.

"If we learn nothing more in the next few days then she seems perfectly safe to be out in the community. She may well be able to help out in the countryside with farm labouring. I fear here in the city she will soon be corrupted into immoral ways, being so simple and easily influenced."

Read agreed to give some of the money to the girl on release. He left Ruthven, Dunckerley and his son lighting more pipes.

After the doctor had left, the three men talked some more about the girl. Dunckerley said that without the portraits he was sure that this girl could not be Felicia, but if that was the case then where had the illegitimate daughter of the Emperor gone? The Emperor was indeed from Bohemia so that answer tied in with it being Felicia, but there was no certainty.

He told Ruthven, "The doctor says that this girl has an injury and it has made her a simpleton. If it is Felicia then I have failed in my promise to Francis to keep her safe. He is dead. Few others know of her existence. If this is not her then we need to look elsewhere in Bristol for her - or maybe my responsibility ends here."

The room began to darken as the men talked and smoked.

Later that evening, inside St Peter's Hospital, the evening chorus of cries and shouts began. It rang down through the corridors and echoed in the rooms. Groans, sighs, terrifying screams, profanities and sobs filled the air and crashed in upon Louisa as she lay on her bed.

The cries of the terrified, the lonely, the deranged and the sick filled the night air. There was little Louisa could do to block it out.

At first she tried to get away from the sounds by putting her hands to her ears. When that didn't work she lay on her bed and pulled the pillow around her ears but it was thin and did little to blank out the noise coming from all parts of the hospital.

She got out of the bed onto the floor, wrapping the sheets around her. But still the terrifying noises of the hospital disturbed her.

The only way she could drown out the squeals and shrieks that were growing in intensity was to make a noise herself.

She started by singing, songs and tunes that she had heard over the years. Fragments of the song she had sung with the girls around the haystack came to her. But as she sang them she felt her own terrible circumstances, locked inside these blank walls, no idea when, or even if, she would ever be outside again. She began to sob. The sobbing turned to shouts and cries and full blown rage. She started to throw the pillow around, clasp her hands to her head. The louder she shouted the less of the cacophony of the hospital she could hear. Louder and louder, more and more out of control. Her rage took over her and she struggled and fought with her own inner demons.

She didn't notice the matron push open the door and look at her. She didn't hear the matron run along the corridor and summon the doctor. The first time she was aware that anyone had heard her cries was when she felt the strong hands of the orderly grab her wrist and pin them to the floor. He then lifted her back onto the bed. The matron grabbed one ankle and in a swift movement tied it to a bedpost and while she shouted and raged swiftly moved to pull her legs apart and move the other ankle to the other bedpost. She looked up and the orderly appeared to be grinning at her as he stretched her arms above her to the top of the bed.

Louisa shouted again and tried with all her might to lift her whole body off the bed but the strength of the orderly was immense and the matron was skilled at binding people tightly.

The doctor entered and shouted at her, "Lay still", but she was not in the mood to listen or obey. The rage was running through her mind. She screamed louder and louder, struggling to free herself.

The doctor spoke to the matron. "Clearly she is suffering from hysteria. As you know we see this a lot in women of this age. It is important to purge the uterus of excess fluids. If you hold her I will administer the treatment and I think you will find she will calm."

The orderly pushed tightly on her arms and asked the doctor, "Shall I manipulate the breasts doctor?" Read nodded and with a swift movement the orderly pulled open the gown Louisa was wearing, exposing her breasts. His elbows pushed hard down on her arms as his fingers clamped tightly on each of her nipples, rubbing and pulling them and then kneading her breasts.

Louisa struggled but couldn't move and looking up all she could see was the stubbled chin of the orderly and beyond that the face of the matron, who occasionally mouthed "be calm" at her. The doctor pulled up her gown and with one arm on her stomach the fingers of both his hands went to work on her most intimate areas. Rubbing and teasing at the sensitive folds. Louisa started to buck and twist to try to avoid the pressure being put on her but she was too tightly held.

The doctor spoke to the matron, "See, we are starting to see the excess fluids from the uterus being expelled from the body."

Louisa tensed as the two men worked away on her. The orderly began to grin and grunt as he worked away at his task. The doctor started to go red with the effort and maintained an attitude of professionalism to the matron but she noticed he bent low to look closely at Louisa's thighs and as he worked faster and faster, he began to sweat and grunt. After a few minutes the matron passed a wooden implement to the doctor and that was pushed against Louisa where the doctor's fingers had been.

Louisa exploded with a gasp. The doctor continued his administrations, but he said loudly, "That's it. Let it out. You'll feel so much better for it."

Louisa slumped gasping and the two men finally stopped their handling of her and stepped away. Dr Read nodded at Matron who ushered the orderly away and pulled Louisa's arm down and covered her breasts once more. Her bottom half was still exposed.

"I can handle her from now, doctor. She has calmed. Once again your methods have worked."

"Yes," said Dr Read, "unfortunately, hysteria is far too common in young women these days so I have had a little practice in the last few years. If she calms in the next few days it seems she can be released. She seems to have no relatives that have an interest in her."

The doctor left the room. Exhausted and terrified, Louisa lay compliant on the bed while the older woman brought her a bowl of water to clean herself and a hot drink. The sounds of the hospital came back to her and when the matron left she put the pillow over her own head once again to try to find some peace. With the pillow over her head she sobbed and sobbed until she fell into a sleep.

Chapter Six

Back to the Haystack

AMY ATKINGS AND Sarah Derrick carried the bundles of sticks they had collected at Bourton Combe in large baskets, walking slowly along the uneven lane back towards their homes. The sticks would be enough for their cooking fires for a day or so and take the chill off their cottages in the evening. There was a distinct autumnal feel to the breeze hissing through the trees in Flax Bourton this afternoon.

Ten yards behind them trotted Johnny Derrick. He carried a lighter load but his feet were plodding in exaggerated tiredness. In truth he was just bored at the ritual and the constant chatter of the two women, who paid him little attention apart from the occasional glance over their shoulders to check he was still making progress.

"It's just not happening for us," said Amy. "I don't think we are going to be blessed with any children at all. I can't keep pretending any more that I'm not barren. I'm getting older by the day and soon William will abandon me for someone who actually can be a proper woman."

"Oh Amy don't speak like that. Look at him," she said, pointing over her shoulder at Johnny who was now dragging his feet dramatically to draw attention to himself, "having children isn't all it is cracked up to be!" She was trying to make light of the conversation but she could tell by her friend's reaction that she had misjudged things. Amy was in no mood to be cheered up.

The two of them walked on in silence. Sarah wished she had not tried to make light of Amy's troubles. Amy realised it was a subject that she kept returning to and feared her friend was bored by the conversation. Both were trying to think of something else to say. It was awkward.

Sarah was first to speak, "Have you heard any more about Louisa?" Amy shook her head, still feeling a little hurt and trying not to show it too much. Sarah was a good friend. But few people understood the desperate feeling she had inside from being childless. No woman was really a woman unless she had borne a child, and no marriage was really a marriage unless it had been blessed with children. That was just the way that the world was. She felt it was her fault.

"I guess she is still in the hospital?" Sarah tried again, "in Bristol".

Amy dragged her thoughts to the conversation, finally saying, "I don't suppose we shall hear any more about her. I think William is going to try to ask around when he is in Bristol. He goes to the Hot Well often and that doctor who took her away is often there. He said he would ask next time he is there."

Sarah called back to Johnny once again and he picked up speed to try to catch the two women up. She stopped until the boy was alongside them.

Just before they got to their home Johnny sat down on the "six mile" stone. It said "Bristol six miles". That was just about the distance to the Bristol Bridge, which was just yards from St Peter's Hospital in the centre of the city. The women let him rest there a few seconds, walking past him and then calling him on.

Soon they were at their homes and went their separate ways, Amy preparing the fire once again and putting a pot of water on the boil ready for the evening meal. She knew that William would be home soon with Jessie and the evening would be short as autumn was beginning to take over from summer as the dominant season.

Inside the house a basket of apples lay waiting to be prepared for preservation. She would peel them and hopefully William would bring some sugar back from Bristol for jam making. Bristol was always plentiful with sugar. Many of the local landowners had a stake in the sugar cane plantations or operated ships that took items to Africa, traded for slaves to work the sugar plantations, and then brought the sugar home. It was good to live so close to

Bristol. There were many goods to be had that other rural areas could not get access to.

Less than an hour later Amy heard the familiar sound of Jessie arriving at the back of her home and William putting the horse away and sorting out the cart. Then she heard the discharge of a shot - this time further away from the house. A few seconds later he was home and kissing her.

"I do hate it every time I hear that gun. Do you really need to carry it?" she said.

"I've told you. It is better to be safe. Bristol is getting busier by the day and everybody seems to be up to some scheme or another. In the old days disputes were settled with the fists but these days so many people have been off to war, over to America or in the army that they turn to weapons first - you just have to protect yourself."

William washed and rested his legs while Amy prepared their meal and soon they were lighting the candles once again as the North Somerset evening set in. They sat in each others arms staring into the fire after their meal.

Amy said, "I'm so sorry I haven't got pregnant. Last month I tried those herbs that woman in Farleigh suggested, but nothing."

William answered, "Yes, it would be good to have a son to keep the family line alive. It will happen soon, I'm sure. These things happen in God's good time, that's what the parish priest said, wasn't it?"

Amy stared more intently at the fire. She just wanted to hear William say that it didn't matter, that he would love her anyway. But that wasn't how things were. Men, understandably, wanted a son; in these rural areas you needed one to share the work burden. She was only half a woman and she knew it.

William's hand was stroking her neck. It was time to try again. But nothing in the world was less appealing to her right now than making love. She kissed him out of duty.

Across the rutted lane Sarah Derrick had set the fire and

had decided to walk with Johnny the short distance across the fields towards Belmont House. At one of the cottages close to the bottom of Belmont Hill there was a smallholding with a large number of chickens, that supplied half the valley with eggs. Sarah had a basket with her and was aiming to buy a dozen or so for cooking and meals that week.

Mrs Bath, who served the eggs, came to the gate and just at that moment William Turner, who owned Belmont House, came past with his friend Joseph Farrell. He was wearing one of his fancy waistcoats that she had heard he bought from Paris and both he and Joseph Farrell wore swords at their waist. They nodded at the ladies and Farrell doffed his hat as they took a small footpath running up the side of the smallholding that led towards a servants entrance into Belmont. The women smiled politely but watched as the men made progress until they were out of earshot.

"Well, there they go…" said Sarah, and both she and Mrs Bath started giggling.

"What to make of them?" said Mrs Bath. "It is no wonder that Hannah More refused his hand. He is more often seen with Joseph Farrell than he ever was with her. The pair of them were in the woods together practically all day at the weekend. You could hear them cackling and chasing about like young lovers. Crazy it is. They go in there sword-fighting and chasing each other around."

"Well…" said Sarah, "you know what they say: it takes all sorts to make a world."

"Sure it does," said Mrs Bath "…and those sorts won't be bothering the likes of you and I none."

Both women laughed as the eggs were exchanged for pennies and the two women said their goodbyes.

Sarah decided to cut back across the fields with her basket and eggs on the return journey to make it a shorter walk for Johnny. It took her past some tall bushes that had branches growing over, forming an avenue above her head. As they rounded a bend the valley started to darken as evening fell and the haystacks came into view. The second one along was where Louisa had spent four nights and thoughts of her came into Sarah's head as it hove into view. Then she saw it.

A movement in the haystack and what looked like some clothing, or a basket, on the floor alongside it. Sarah kept her eyes on the haystack and as she got nearer she was sure there was something there and there seemed to be movement on a number of occasions; not the sort of movement you might see from a bird, or a badger or a fox. This was big movement. There was a person in there. Sarah slowed and approached cautiously. She wasn't afraid. She walked these paths and lanes all the time. But she was curious as to who was rooting about in the haystack that Louisa had vacated some days before. She put her hand out to grasp Johnny's hand just in case.

They were right beside the haystack before she could see properly. It was Louisa, settled back into the same space. She didn't notice Sarah and Johnny approach. She appeared to be hanging some of the trinkets back around the haystack and making it comfortable.

"Louisa!" Sarah shouted, and almost immediately wished she hadn't, as Louisa jumped out of her skin and leapt up as if she was going to take flight. Her darting, scared eyes met the familiar eyes of Sarah Derrick and, still gasping, heart thumping from the shock of the shout, she opened her mouth in a laugh.

"What are you doing here? I thought you had been taken away to hospital?"

"I stay here," said Louisa, "it is nice here. There are only bad things in houses and in hospitals. Let me stay here. I have some money." Louisa started to go for her bag and Sarah chuckled at the thought of Louisa trying to pay her some rent for the haystack.

"You settle down. I will tell Amy you are here. Do the hospital know you are here? How did you get here?"

"They gave me money. They took me in a carriage out of the city and then I walk here. They gave me money for a room. But I don't want a room. I want to stay here. This is a beautiful place and the people are kind. You are kind. We can sing and dance some more. There is no happiness but in liberty and fresh air."

Sarah was shaking her head at the ridiculousness of the situation, unsure what the Atkings' would think - or for that matter everyone else in the village. It was a complete mystery how Louisa had once again landed up in the haystack, but Sarah knew that most people locally would accept her back. The world had not been so bright since the day she was taken off to hospital and there was less to talk about without her being the focus of village gossip.

Sarah took a look into the nook that Louisa had created in the haystack. She had once again got all her possessions out and put them around. She had some clothes drying from a branch stuck in the ground. Her large bag, which had been on the floor outside when Sarah approached, had now been moved under cover, to be sure it was a comfortable and cosy place to bed down for the night. Louisa smiled at Johnny who hid his face behind his mother's skirts.

Sarah wished Louisa goodnight and darkness was creeping in as she walked away up towards the rear of the Atkings' cottage. Louisa watched mother and son walk away, then climbed out of the haystack and went to the far side. Reaching underneath she felt the oilskin parcel she was looking for. She pulled it out and took it back to her cosy place. She unwrapped it and inside was a blue silk purse containing pictures. She took one that showed a woman half-concealed by a veil and lay back in the haystack looking at it. She was happy to see those eyes in the picture once again.

It was dark by the time Sarah got to the Atkings' door and she was uncertain whether to disturb them that night. She hesitated but then decided that the news she had to impart was just too exciting to leave until the morning. After all, the Atkings' may get up early and discover Louisa themselves and that would ruin the pleasure she was about to get from imparting the news to them.

Amy was astonished when she heard and wanted to rush down to the haystack to check for herself but William insisted there was nothing to gain by going out in the dark and they would check on Louisa in the morning. Sarah left, satisfied that she had been the bringer of big news.

The next day dawned dry and fairly sunny with misty wispy clouds covering the sky around Flax Bourton. William was due to head into Bristol first thing so as soon as he could he wandered down to the haystack. Louisa was asleep in the hay, her fine arms bare and her long slender fingers gripping some stalks, her head shaded by an overhang in the haystack. She looked at perfect peace.

Back at the cottage Amy and William discussed what would happen about the visitor. William wasn't convinced by the story that Sarah had gleaned from Louisa.

"I can't believe the doctor would let her just wander out of the hospital and come back here. There is no way they would give her money. She must have escaped somehow and she must have stolen the money or got it by some ill-gotten means."

Amy was torn. Part of her was pleased that the excitement of the Maid of the Haystack had returned. The four days she had sat in the haystack had been quite fun and she had taken a shine to Louisa, who was a bit of fun in the monotony of life in rural Somerset.

"Why don't you call in at Hot Wells and check with them there? They may be missing her again. The other thing is where is she going to stay? Those haystacks have to come down soon and the farmers here can't afford to have her sleeping there. She says she has money but she doesn't have enough rent to live there, I wouldn't imagine."

William hitched Jessie up to the cart and set off for Bristol, once again thoughts of the crazy visitor going through his head as he drove into the city.

Just past Dowry Square in Hotwells he saw Maggie Harrison walking across the road, carrying some kind of basket in her arms. It looked heavy. He shouted after her and she threw the basket up onto his cart and hopped up alongside it for a lift for the last few hundred yards to the spa offices.

William told her about Louisa returning and she said she had heard nothing but that Dr Read was, indeed, in the spa that day dispensing treatments and she would speak to him to see if he could throw any light on what had happened. As the cart pulled to a halt, she jumped down, grabbed the basket and swiftly went inside. William tied the reins to a rail and put a nosebag onto Jessie to keep her occupied as much as to feed her and he entered the spa offices, once again taking off his hat.

Just inside there was a noisy group of around a dozen London types and holding forth in front of them he recognised Patty More, youngest of the More sisters. She was highly animated and telling some story that had the group - mostly men - in stitches. He knew her as the sister of Hannah More, who had been spurned by the much-older William Turner of Belmont. The story was that after he had proposed to her three times but never gone through with it, Hannah More had been made ill by the scandal and gone to Uphill by the sea at Weston-super-Mare but was now frequently around the rich and famous from London.

The group were so full of themselves that they didn't notice William and he sat down, hat on his lap, to watch their antics, while he waited for Maggie to come back with news. From their conversation he gathered they were actors in some play at the Theatre Royal in Bristol - it had apparently gone "exceedingly well" last night and now they were with young Patty waiting for their spa treatments. One was telling an over-dramatic story about a missed cue line at a theatre in Bath a few days ago, which seemed to send all the others into haw-hawing at immense volume. The loud voices, name-dropping and over-dramatic actions of the group seemed to reach a crescendo and echo all around the room - and then William saw Maggie ducking through the group towards him. She rolled her eyes at him and sat down beside him.

"I won't be sorry when this lot go through to the treatments," she said, safe in the knowledge they were so engrossed with each other that they wouldn't hear her insult.

"Doctor says she was released yesterday and she was given some money from a benefactor. Apparently the benefactor was looking for someone that met her description but it isn't her, but he gave some sort of gift to help her out anyway. The doctor says she has been treated for hysteria and has improved and she probably has an old head injury that accounts for her being doolally sometimes.

"He says she's not dangerous and there is no reason to keep her there and the benefactor wasn't prepared to pay for her confinement, so the hospital released her. Who knows how she found her way back to the haystack. They aren't going to do anything else so I guess you just have to kick her out and send her on her way!"

"I guess we do," said William. Maggie held up a finger and danced through the group of actors once again and returned with two drinks in glasses.

"We might as well settle down and enjoy the show before you go," she said laughing and they settled back with their drinks to watch the antics of the London crowd. Around 10 minutes passed before the group were called through and Maggie and William laughed at the over-the-top explanations of how "fabulous" everything seems to be in the spa, which they could hear even after the group were through into the next room.

William spent most of the day in Bristol. He stopped by the

docks and got a little money from helping to transport some sacks from a ship that had been unloaded. It was just around the quayside and two of the ships' crew sat up with him. They said they were glad to be back in Bristol after months away. They had sailed to Africa with metal pots and pans and then had been on board as the ship was loaded with black African slaves bound for the Americas.

One of them said, "It is getting worse and worse on those journeys. Too many slaves packed in and it's not a cargo you want to be dealing with. Then when you get back here there are a lot of people giving you stick for it. The last leg was good though, we had a fair easterly all the way back and just the crew and sacks of proper goods. We've done too many now - if they want experienced crews on those slave ships they need to pay a bit more, and make the conditions better for us."

It was the usual gossip and chat around the port and William headed back that evening looking forward to the latest instalment in the saga of the maid sitting in the haystack around the back of his home.

Half the village had gathered in the evening light when he got home - including Amy - and after letting Jessie loose in the field he walked over to the group to see what was happening.

Amy turned to him. "Any news?" He told the assembled group about his visit to the spa and the message that had come from the doctor. That seemed to end a a lot of speculation that had been going on about the returning Louisa.

But the men in the group were pretty adamant, and William backed them. She had to be told to move on as the hay was needed and there was no way they could afford to have her cost them money.

The group broke up and there was some kind of resolve that Louisa could stay there for a day or so, then move on. All the time the conversations and discussions were going on, Louisa seemed blissfully unaware tidying around the haystack. Either she did not understand what they were saying or she just didn't care.

After a short time people started to drift away but Amy and Sarah went over to Louisa to try to engage with her. At first she kept her gaze away from them, ignoring them as a small child might when you were trying to attract their attention to send them to bed.

But after the two village women started helping her to tidy some of her belongings Louisa smiled and sat with them and at last seemed ready to talk.

Amy confronted her. "What are your plans now? Where will you go?"

Louisa looked about her, slightly forlorn. "I stay here. I have some money for you." She started fiddling in her bag and offered coins to the women who looked at each other.

"I am happy here. I have come a long way to find this place with good people."

Amy and Sarah exchanged glances again. There was still a small group, mostly the women who had joined in the singing at the haystack days before, standing and chatting as the sun went down. Their topics had already moved on from Louisa as they caught up on village gossip.

Sarah took Louisa's hand. "Look, you must understand that this land is not ours. We simply live here and we have to pay rent for our cottages and the land here to the owner Mr Sparrow. The land provides us with food and some income but we need all of it to survive. If you are living here then we will have to pay extra to Mr Sparrow, but he may not allow it even if we think it is a good idea."

Louisa looked confused. The two women weren't convinced she had understood the situation but at least they had told her about it. Louisa was calm. She turned away from them and curled up in the hay. They took that as their signal to rejoin the others.

In truth few of them knew James Sparrow well. His family had owned the land for many years. But his wife, Letitia, had a young family, including a one-year-old daughter, Lucy, and she had been meeting with other women with young children for support and to let the youngsters play together. Before marriage she had been Letitia Popham. She had moved to Flax Bourton from her family home in West Bagborough, Somerset, many miles further south and had tried to make friends locally as she knew few people in the new area where she had moved into her husband's ancestral home. As the men drifted off to talk amongst themselves the women conspired to talk to Letitia Sparrow and see if some arrangement could be made for Louisa to stay longer in the haystack.

It was two days later that a painted carriage stopped in Flax Bourton. It was the type usually reserved for lavish parties and social events. Out stepped Letitia Sparrow with a nursemaid carrying little Lucy. The maid pulled on a hand and out stepped four-year-old Henrietta. There were older children at school but this was the domestic scene at Castle House where the land-owning family lived.

Letitia had been told about the plight of the woman living in the haystack and had decided to come to see for herself what was going on. As the parade of finery moved across the fields towards the haystack Louisa spotted them and, seeing the children, immediately beamed at them. Taking a small corn dolly that she had tied to her temporary home, she went down on her haunches and offered it at arms length to little Henrietta. The toddler ran towards her beaming with joy and by the time Letitia Sparrow and the nursemaid reached the haystack the little one was sat quite happily next to Louisa playing with the doll.

Sarah had spotted the carriage arrive and had knocked for Amy and the two women were now making their way across the field to join in. As they neared they both bobbed in little curtseys in deference to their superior and were both impressed at the fine cut of her gown.

Letitia Sparrow was immediately charmed by Louisa. She

saw a woman wearing a gown as fine as her own, some years younger than herself; a woman who was more concerned about keeping a young child happy than paying respect to a superior. In fact everything about Louisa seemed to indicate that she was someone of more noble birth than the farm women who were now standing just a few feet away seemingly scared to speak.

Louisa looked Letitia straight in the eye, "A beautiful child," she said, indicating Henrietta. She patted Henrietta's head then moved over to look at little Lucy, who was now sitting on the grass between the legs of the nursemaid.

"Two beautiful children. You are very lucky!" she said and beamed at her visitor. At this Amy stepped forward and introduced Letitia to Louisa, attempting to explain that this was the lady of the household that owned the haystack. But Louisa was already back with little Henrietta playing dollies and making the toddler laugh.

Letitia looked at Amy. "So, I am told that she has been living here for some days. She came back from the hospital is that correct?"

"Yes ma'am," said Amy. "She just appeared here one night asking for milk and after four days we arranged for her to go into St Peter's Hospital in Bristol. But, although they believe she is a maniac of some sort, she is harmless and can be quite fun. Nobody is sure where she came from. We have all taken quite a shine to her really but she is showing no inclination to move on."

Sarah joined in. "She says she likes it here. She feels safe here. We think she comes from a foreign land. Sometimes her English is not good. But she understands most things. She has a small amount of money and....er.....some of us are willing to put some other money to it if she can be permitted to stay here."

Letitia didn't hesitate. "Of course, I understand. She is beautiful and those clothes are from London or maybe even Paris. I'll have a word with my husband. I'm sure some arrangement can be made. Is there anyone she can move in with?"

Amy spoke. "That's the problem really, she won't go inside. She wants to live in the haystack. She is only happy in a haystack. Can you work out how much it is to rent a haystack?"

Letitia shook her head amused and the other women, including the nursemaid, giggled at the preposterous idea of renting a haystack. Letitia agreed that she would speak to her husband and try to come up with an agreed sum to allow Louisa to stay legally in the haystack for as long as she wanted. The women agreed that it needed to be a month-by-month deal as none of them knew whether Louisa might suddenly take flight and move on. Or maybe her past was soon to catch up with her.

- Chapter Seven -

Belmont

LOUISA SOON BECAME a fixture of the local scene in Flax Bourton. The local women each put pennies in towards her rent and small amounts came from Louisa herself, firstly from the dwindling sum she had been given at the hospital and then from money given by visitors. Often the local gentry, prompted out of curiosity to visit after hearing stories from the Sparrow family, would give a little to Louisa.

Villagers became quite used to seeing carriages pull up and gentlefolk take the short walk to the permanent haystack. Many handed over small gifts and trinkets which Louisa hung around the haystack. They would hang there for days, weeks or months and then she would occasionally hand them out herself as gifts to children or others she took a shine to.

Each visitor she greeted with a beaming smile. Sometimes she sang and danced or ran around the haystack and it was her joyous, bright, breezy, carefree nature that had a charm for those whose own lives were governed by the pressures of duty or work.

Letitia Sparrow visited often with her two small daughters, and sometimes when not in school, her older children. They played happily with Louisa and had fun running around the haystack. Often the visits were prompted by the children asking if they could go to see the "Maid of the Haystack" as a treat.

Sometimes they brought food for Louisa and others dropped by with treats, things for her to eat, and clothing, although her outermost clothes seemed to always retain some of the finery that she had first arrived in.

Through the winter of 1776 Louisa insisted on staying in the haystack. When the frosts came Amy and others brought her blankets and soup and her "home" expanded with donated goods, taking on the air of an enchanted cave or grotto and making it even more interesting for the chattering classes who gathered there on the bright winter days when there was better weather.

By late January 1777, William Atkings was finding his visits to Bristol increasingly fraught. A series of arson attacks on ships and explosions in warehouses had caused terror and nervousness among the people. It was said that foreign agents with sympathies in America were carrying out the attacks, as they had done in Portsmouth.

Suddenly it was not so easy to get the casual work around the docks and suspicions were running high of just about everyone who was in the area.

The explosions started on ships and then some warehouses went up in smoke. There was tension and talk of terrorists. Soldiers were on the streets hunting for those who might be undermining the wealth of the city.

Everywhere that William went there was fear and edginess where there had once been calm. He was well known for travelling around the city. He had access to many warehouses and he often helped load or unload ships. He was sometimes in the homes of the gentry; sometimes in the hostelries and mixing with the rougher elements of the city; a man who appeared to have access to anywhere.

Everyone feared that there could be another explosion at any moment - and this one could be fatal. Extra guards were put on warehouses and ships at anchor. Suddenly paperwork was being checked and double-checked. Then a rumour went around that someone was trying to poison the city's water supply and it became difficult just trying to get a drink. William started taking his own water to drink on his trips into Bristol. It just wasn't the same for him any more.

The King's troops were sent to Bristol. Many were hosted at the Masonic Hall by Dunckerley and the great and good of the city. Investigations into who was setting the fires continued. Clues were followed up and a name was given to the authorities, again and again; it was Aitken.

William Atkings was just pulling out of the powder warehouse with another load for the Hot Well when a figure appeared in front of him and called him to halt. He was wary, even moreso when he noticed two other men nearby. Could these be the terrorists? He slid his hand under the blanket. He knew he had only one shot and that would not be enough against a group like this. He pulled the gun out and immediately regretted his decision. He was surrounded by armed men, shouting at him. He feared for his life. One false move and he was dead. He threw his gun to the floor.

Jessie panicked as the men moved in on him. One of the men held onto her reins to hold her still as others wrestled William from his seat and pinned him to the floor, one giving him a whack across the face for good measure.

William was taken to the New Gaol by the men. They were acting for the King and it soon became apparent under questioning that the reason for his detention was that he had been identified as possibly the wanted terrorist Aitken. It was a tense few hours talking to officials and he was questioned in detail about his movements around the docks in recent weeks. Atkings could not remember many of the dates in detail but he admitted he had been close to many of the places where there had been fires and explosions but that he was a simple man from the nearby rural area with no sympathies with America, knowledge of explosives or motivation to get involved.

Finally, at the end of the day, someone in authority agreed that he should be allowed to go back to where he claimed to live, so that his story could be checked out. It was agreed that he would be accompanied to Flax Bourton. Two soldiers rode behind William who was on his cart. Behind that was a Government official in a carriage with armed outriders. They followed him as he headed a parade back to his home village. Amy was terrified to see the officials who went from cottage to cottage checking out William's story. Finally satisfied they formally released him.

Before heading back into the city the soldiers and the Government official went to visit the haystack and meet with Louisa. Some of the neighbours had mentioned that the only foreign person they knew nearby was the amiable girl, who could not possibly be anything to do with the fires and explosions as she had not left her unusual home now for more than eight months.

It was a pleasant 30 minutes with the soldiers laying down their guns and chatting to the village children and enjoying the sight of this lively and amusing girl playing around the haystack and singing country songs to entertain them. William, his face swollen and sore, sat, still visibly shaken by his ordeal, holding on to Amy.

Amy said, "Promise me you won't ever carry that stupid gun again."

"I'm not likely to. They took it away from me. I'm never going armed again. To be honest I'm not sure I ever want to set foot in Bristol again. I'm going to see if I can make a living out here through our friends and the land-owners. The city is not for me. There is too much violence and fear on the streets. Things are changing fast and I'm not a young man any more."

Within days news spread that a man named James Aitken - nicknamed John the Painter - had been arrested for the terrorism in Bristol and Portsmouth. He was hanged later that year. Simply having a similar name - and not knowing how to spell it - had put William briefly in the frame for terrible crimes. Aitken was Scottish and soon after his arrest the authorities realised that Atkings, clearly a local man, could not be their suspect. But the fact he had pulled a gun and had been seen in many of the relevant places at the relevant times had put his liberty - even his life - in great danger.

The incident meant that, in the late spring of 1777, many little groups of soldiers and other officials from Bristol started arriving to spend a morning or afternoon with the Maid of the Haystack. Her lovable lunacy was infectious, and the fact that as the days got a little warmer she would skip around with her buttons undone and breasts lolling into view was also popular with the all-male groups. But it seemed that usually, when things got raucous and were beginning to get out-of-hand, Amy, Sarah or one of the other women who lived nearby would head down to the haystack and give the boys from out of town a talking to and they would calm down and head off.

Mostly, the visits were prompted by those who had seen her before and the curiosity of the mysterious girl who had chosen such an odd lifestyle.

With tensions high in the city many of the fashionable folk at the Hot Well decided it was safer and calmer to head into the countryside for their amusement and, around March 1777, an organised visit of 20 folk from the Hot Well suddenly descended on Flax Bourton. After drinks in The Bell Inn they took their picnic baskets to the stack yard where Louisa was living in the haystack and sat around singing songs and telling stories.

Louisa took it in turns to visit each of the little groups as they picnicked. They shared some of their food with her, she danced and sang and it made for a great day out.

The whole adventure gave William Atkings an idea. He went to see Maggie Harrison and between them they organised more trips for groups from the Spa in Bristol to travel out to Flax Bourton and spend a day in the countryside to see "The Maid of The Haystack".

It meant less visits into the city for William and he and Amy made small amounts from providing refreshments and taking a penny from each visitor in return for telling the tale of how Louisa had arrived and introducing them to her.

Louisa chatted to people but if questioned about her background or how she came to be there never once slipped-up by saying something other than her usual answers; that she liked it in the haystack and that she had bad experiences of living indoors. Gossip about the strange occurrence in Flax Bourton grew as more than a year passed with Louisa still tucked into her haystack home.

One visitor did manage to have a curious conversation with Louisa in German. Her name was Maayke. She was a gentlewoman, who originally came from Altona, a borough of Hamburg in Germany. Her husband was a Danish sea captain, whose ship berthed in Bristol. While at the spa, she joined a trip with some other women to see the Maid of the Haystack.

Detecting a German accent she spoke to Louisa in German and Louisa replied clearly in German telling her that she had lived in Sleswick in Germany and had been in a convent from which she had escaped with her lover. She said she had spent time in Hamburg and clearly knew some places there. It was a short conversation, as they were interrupted.

Although Belmont Estate was less than a mile away from Flax Bourton, William Turner and his live-in friend Joseph Farrell knew little of what was going on in the nearby village. William was all too aware of the gossip from the locals following his failure to marry Hannah More. Hannah was a great catch for any man, she was beautiful, witty and intelligent. She was tough, independent and spoke her own mind. She was not the type to be a loyal, devoted wife, cooking and cleaning. She was interested in poetry and art and nature.

That was what had attracted Turner to her. He had first met her because two of his female cousins had attended the boarding school in Bristol run by Hannah and her sisters. They had invited Hannah and her younger sister Patty to the Belmont Estate in the holidays and Turner had immediately been smitten by the young woman.

It was the first time he had these feelings for a woman. He and Joe had a secret that could not be mentioned. They knew many others in Bristol, men who liked men, but it was never spoken about openly as their practices were regarded as a sin against God. Hannah was many years younger than Turner and he saw her as a great companion and maybe also an answer to the whispers about him not having a wife.

His masculinity was rarely questioned as he was an accomplished swordsman and boxer in his early days. Even now he was older he would often go to the Fencing Rooms over the Market Gate in High Street. They were kept by a man named Chebas and, although it was often Joe he would spar with, he was known for taking on all-comers with the foil.

Hannah loved the grounds at Belmont and Turner and Joe enthusiastically designed little areas of the garden to make the most of the magnificent views across the valley towards the sea. On fine days you could see the Mendip Hills on the left and sweep your eye to the right to take in the islands in the Bristol Channel and the hills of Wales beyond.

They first created a "view" by cutting back some branches and placed a seat so that they could sit and look at the ever-changing scenery while the young cousins played in the woods. Soon Hannah was writing marvellous poems about the view and they got more ambitious.

Egged on by Joe, William Turner created wooden sign boards with Hannah's poems on them that could be strategically placed in the woods and walkways they had made around the estate. When fashionable friends came from Bristol they were able to have readings of the poetry on the very spot where Hannah had composed them.

Carried away with the excitement of it all, one evening when Joe was back at the house, William Turner had gone down on one knee and proposed to Hannah and she said "yes".

Joe saw it as a betrayal but William sought to persuade him that they could somehow live in a happy threesome. It was a large estate. There was room for Joe to live near. William's marriage to the young and beautiful Hannah would be perfect cover for their sins. They knew other married men in the city who had successfully had sex-less marriages with women while keeping a male lover.

The problem was that Hannah was becoming increasingly famous. She was adored by theatrical types for her writing. William Turner wanted privacy and he was not keen on the gossip that kept surrounding him as three times a date for the wedding was set and three times he said he could not go through with it after Joe had insisted that it would not work.

By now Hannah was spending much time alone in a little folly they had built for her in the grounds. Together they found a rock in the grounds where rust-coloured water seeped out staining the stone. Hannah wrote a poem called The Bleeding Rock and Joe and Turner wrote it out once again on boards and added it to the attractions at Belmont.

The whole thing had ended in tears when Turner said for the fourth time that he was ready to marry Hannah and she confronted him with the real reason he would not marry her - he loved Joe more than he loved her.

They agreed to part. She was devastated and upset and ill with worry that the scandal might come out. William Turner was also keen that the scandal would not be made public and offered £200 a year to keep Hannah in a comfortable income for life. It was not unusual for those who had been betrothed to receive compensation of this kind. She refused at first but her sisters persuaded her that they could do much good with the money. Their break-up had been in 1773. By the time Louisa had moved into the haystack Hannah had grown even more popular in society and Turner and Joe were living quietly on the Belmont Estate, still with the reminders of the six years with the genius lady-friend around the gardens.

The two men often went into Bristol to the Nag's Head in Wine Street where they joined other Tories and Jacobites and toasted the Pretender in a ceremony on their knees.

On Tuesday nights they attended the Masonic Lodge in Bristol for the most secret of secret meetings. Among the other men who attended was Thomas Dunckerley Junior, who had now turned 20 and was powerful as the son of a man now publicly being spoken about as a brother to the King and just about at the top of the Masonic tree. He was one of the organisers of the meetings. As his father was universally accepted by the group as the illegitimate son of a king that made him, in turn, royalty and that was an attraction in itself to the fops and social-climbers who went to the secret meeting.

It was in late 1777 that William Turner and Joseph Farrell went to their usual weekly meeting of men who liked the company of other men; a secret society within a secret society. Most men attended in couples but there were some single men attending and it was a place where men could be more obvious about their tastes and be assured that those around them were like-minded.

This night music was being played and some poetry being read. William liked to sit quiet at these events but Joe liked to perform and at one point he read a poem by Hannah More, inspired by Failand Hill on which the Belmont Estate stood. It was called "Inscription on a Beautiful Retreat Called Fairy Bower".

There were lots of smiles and nods at the reference to fairies - one of the secret words the group used to identify each other. The term had been adopted by effeminate men as their type often played the parts of fairies in stage dramas. Joe settled down next to William while another man took up a flute and began to play for everyone's entertainment. Dunckerley came over to sit with them.

"Good to see you Joe and Will," said Dunckerley. "That was a great poem. Do you see much of Hannah these days?"

William looked at his feet. "No…but she keeps in touch. She sends me a copy every time she has a book published."

"Yeah we are building up something of a library at the

moment," said Joe. "It is good reading. She is in London these days staying with Garrick and all the high society types. She has a play called Percy that is apparently packing them in to the theatre. She is an amazing woman and her fame is growing in London. Her books are interesting but hey, young Dunckerley, did you not say that you had access to some banned erotica? I heard from one of the guys here at the last meeting that they borrowed a stash and it was pretty sensational."

"Oh yes, it is in one of my father's safes. There are quite a few tracts in there that you would find entertaining," young Dunckerley said with a wicked smile.

"Do you have 'Memoirs of a Woman of Pleasure', about the adventures of the harlot Fanny Hill? I've heard the descriptions in there are to be enjoyed."

"Oh yes," said Dunckerley, "I have read that one. Have you not? There is one particular passage describing the size and shape of a messenger boy she seduces that you really must read. It is a work of genius. It's by John Clelland. He really writes such mouth-watering descriptions. I'll go and find it for you. You can borrow the stash."

Dunckerley went to a safe in another part of the building. Inside there were a number of documents, all with lurid titles and containing sexual content, aimed at exciting men. He found an anonymous Masonic bag to put the items in and took them back to the couple who were now relaxed and chatting to others.

"Keep these private and return them when you have finished with them. Memoirs Of A Woman of Pleasure is there and there are three or four others. All of them are banned so keep them away from anyone who might cause problems. Enjoy them!" He winked and with that went across the room to chat to a handsome young man in a periwinkle wig who had caught his eye, standing alone by the drinks table.

The two men took their bag of erotic literature back to Belmont House and threw it on the bedroom table, where it stayed that evening as they - buoyed by having an evening where they could be so open - got into bed and made love.

It was the next evening that the two men poured a drink and lay on the bed and took out the papers in the Masonic bag. There were a number of manuscripts, all seemingly well-thumbed. They laid them out on the bed. One was called "An Essay on Woman" and another was "The Hussar And His Prick". There was the promised "Memoirs of a Woman of Pleasure" and one called "A Secret Narrative of the Emperor's Daughter".

The men decided that they would read - and maybe act out some scenes from - "Memoirs of A Woman of Pleasure". Soon the manuscript was abandoned and the pair were simply writhing and enjoying each other's bodies.

Over the next few days and weeks it became a regular way for them to spice up their relationship and enjoy the dark nights at Belmont.

"Memoirs of a Woman of Pleasure" took more than a week for them to finish as they read through it in sections, making love once both were aroused by a scene. Then they would move on to the next manuscript.

The stories they read described in detail the sexual exploits of harlots. There were passages about sex between two women, or two men or even small groups. They took each of the scripts in turn and it was a few weeks later that they picked up "A Secret Narrative of the Emperor's Daughter".

It was disappointing. There were no descriptions of sex. This was not a work of erotica. It was a completely different type of document. It was an account of La Freulen Felicia and how she should be protected by the Masonic Order. Clearly this had been put into the safe to keep it away from prying eyes but it had somehow found itself amongst the erotica.

Joe discarded the paper and moved on to one of the others for their night-time wrestle. But a few days later, when Joe was out and rain was hammering against the windows of Belmont

House, William Turner started reading the account. The more he read, the more sensational the story seemed to be.

This is what he read…

THE EMPEROR'S DAUGHTER

A Secret Narrative of the Emperor's Daughter

ON NO ACCOUNT must this paper be copied or passed on to someone outside of the Masonic Order. It is a true account of matters concerning the Holy Roman Emperor Francis I, Master Mason of the Grand Lodge of England. Emperor Francis I was initiated in 1731 by British Ambassador Philip Stanhope at The Hague.

I, Provincial Grand Master, was assigned the special task of protecting La Freulen Felicia by the Emperor. This paper should only be placed in the hands of members of the Masonic Order who have duties concerning La Freulen Felicia while she is under the care and protection of the Order in England.

The narrative following sets out in chronological order the sequence of events that brought La Freulen Felicia to England, the circumstances that led to her current difficult disposition and why she must be kept safe at all costs. This narrative is to be passed to Lodge members when relevant in order to inform them of the true background and circumstances concerning Le Freulen Felicia, who must be protected, kept safe and her location secret.

Declaration

The woman that we have brought to England was born in 1755. Her mother was Maria Wilhelmina von Neipperg (now Princess of Auersperg), a Maid of Honour to Empress Maria Theresa. She is the result of a liaison between the Maid of Honour with Francis I, Holy Roman Emperor. She is therefore the Emperor's daughter and as such should be treated as Royalty.

At the time of her birth Francis I and his wife Empress Maria Theresa had just announced the birth of their new daughter Marie Antoinette (now Queen of France). The Empress knew nothing of the illegitimate child, born within days of Marie Antoinette. The Emperor arranged a secret home for the baby, so that she could be brought up without any scandal affecting the Emperor and Empress. The Emperor arranged for money to be supplied to support the child through her life with a plan drawn up that through childhood she would be prepared for a life in a nunnery.

With no knowledge of her birth, and in the confines of a Holy place, she would have a quiet, religious and useful life serving God. This would also ensure that no scandal fell upon any of the European households.

As a little girl she lived in a sequestered house in a rural and quiet part of Bohemia and was put into the care of two women, one aged around 50 and the other aged around 30. The details of these women have not been revealed to us. The little girl called the older woman Mama and the younger woman Catherine, and those are the names we shall use in this narrative.

A Jesuit priest was assigned to keep watch over Felicia as she grew, sworn to secrecy through the confessional. He visited her regularly through her childhood to teach her the catechism and instruct her on the ways of God. His role was to prepare her for her life in a nunnery. During one visit he discovered that Mama had begun instructing her on reading and writing and he ended this as it had been agreed that she should only be prepared for the religious life that was her fate.

In a short while the Empress became aware of gossip in court of her husband's affair and she ordered that Felicia's mother, Maria Wilhelmina von Neipperg, should marry

Johann Adam Joseph Prince von Auersperg in April 1756, a man who has no interest in women. This was convenient for both parties. It ended much of the gossip. The Emperor and Princess of Auersperg continued their relationship in secret. It was the Princess who asked the Emperor to check on their daughter as she was curious how the child was growing and as a result the Emperor began to visit the child without the knowledge of the Empress. He first took the opportunity to visit with one of his attendants while hunting in the area where she was living. He found the child to be a charming little girl and he sat her on his knee and told her she must be submissive and obey her Mama and those who told her how to live her life.

Eighteen months later he visited again while hunting in the area, with the same attendant once again with him. The girl was now a curious child and asked him about Masonic insignia he wore around his neck. He told her it was the insignia of an officer and she should respect anyone with such insignia as she was the daughter of an officer herself. They spent such an agreeable time together that the little girl began to cry when he was leaving and this affected the Emperor a great deal and he promised her he would return soon. The whole visit had made him doubt the course of action he had taken for the girl's future.

He discussed his visit with the Princess, who, as a result, herself made a short visit to see the child and was upset to think of such a fair child being condemned to a convent.

The Emperor was unable to return for another two years due to illness and at a third and final meeting he made a decision that sending the girl to a convent was not right. He told the girl he had been unable to come to see her because he had been ill and that prompted her to start crying once again and she told him she loved him.

Everything changed on that last visit to see her. He had seen the Princess just before and she had been fretting about their daughter, saying there must be some other way than to put her in a convent. There must be some way to give her freedom and a good life. He was not well. He was feeling his age and it seemed wrong to condemn this beautiful, lively, lovely girl to a life in a nunnery.

Left alone with her he had told her he would take care of her, would make her rich and happy, would give her a palace, money, and attendants; that her domestics would wear yellow and blue liveries. With every word he spoke her face lit up. She was more of a princess than any girl he had ever seen - and he had seen so many princesses in his time. He asked her if she would like to see the Queen and her reply was, "What is a queen?"

He had told her, "A queen is the first lady in the kingdom, and highly to be respected as such, you would love her much if you knew her - but you will never be able to meet her."

He gave her three small pictures, all of which were painted by Jean-Etienne Liotard and mounted in jewell-encrusted frames. One was a portrait of himself, another was the Empress and the third was of Felicia's mother, the Princess - in this one the face was concealed by a veil so he felt safe in giving her the picture and telling her it was her mother. The pictures were all placed in a blue silk purse that he also stuffed with money for her. He left in tears promising her that she should soon be happy.

It was at this point that the Emperor engaged the help of his brethren in the Masonic Order. He made arrangements through his fellow Masons for money that would have been sent to the convent in France to be instead sent to the girl herself as long as she could live anonymously under the name of Felicia Juliana de Schonau, and be given a new home in France or England. The Brethren found a suitable home for her in France.

The priest was instructed to deliver the girl to a ship in the harbour of Hamburgh and hand her over to people he believed would take the girl to the convent. In fact it was arranged for members of the Masonic order to be there and take her to a new life at the accommodation that had been found in France.

Catherine and Mama had been telling the girl what to expect in a religious life and this made her fearful of her fate. Sadly the Emperor died in August 1765 when the girl was 10-years-old, and before the arrangements were fully put into place but I, Thomas Dunckerley, a trusted member of the Brethren and myself the illegitimate son of a Monarch, was charged with ensuring that his wishes were carried out; that Felicia would indeed be taken to a safe place to live and the Emperor's secret would never be revealed.

A fund was set up for her to receive money for life. On his passing all of the financial affairs of the Emperor were administered by Johann Karl Phillip, Graf von Cobenzl, and the arrangements for the girl were amongst a large number of funds that the Emperor had put in place for payments around the world. It was arranged that these would be paid through the Masonic network and used to support the girl in her life as long as she remained unmarried and the story of her illegitimacy was not revealed.

I, Thomas Dunckerley, made arrangements through the Masonic network, for Felicia's move to Bordeaux, where she would stay with a trusted Mason, a German merchant, and his family. The Jesuit Priest was simply told that a convent in France had been found for her, far away from the scandal of the birth. The priest was unaware that the girl was actually to be moved to a house.

Mama and Catherine were calling Felicia by the pet-name Licia and this was the name she preferred to tell people when asked.

In 1766, the priest informed Felicia that her Protector who had visited her had died and that she was now of age to be moved to a convent in France. He told her they would be making the journey in a few days and that he had to measure her for some clothes. He brought a ribbon tape-measure with him to measure her.

A week later he arrived back in a carriage and brought with him four dresses, two pelisses, a black and a red gown - these were the finest garments that the girl had ever had.

The priest said they were to leave for Hamburgh the next day and from there she would board a ship to take her to the convent. Wearing a blue pelisse the next day she and Catherine got into the carriage.

It was a sad parting between Mama and her "little Licia". Both were crying and wailing and waving until the very last moment. Little Licia was scared of the future. Mama had told her about the hours and hours of praying; the early mornings; the frugal lifestyle and how it was unlikely she would be able to run in the fields and lay on her back in the haystacks watching the clouds, which she had enjoyed so much during her rural upbringing. She felt as if she was being carried off to prison, not to a new life.

Licia vowed to escape from the carriage but although they had three stops on their way to Hamburgh there was no time when the priest was not within a few yards and none of the places they alighted for drinks and food and to stretch their legs were big enough for her to feel she could make an escape and get away.

At Hamburgh they were all staying in a lodging house for one night and on an evening walk she was shown the ship that the priest said would take her to the convent in France. Later back at the lodgings she waited until Catherine was asleep in the room, made a little parcel of the gowns and some linen, took the silk purse with the three pictures and 100 ducats which she had been given by the Emperor, and left quietly - dawn was just breaking and Catherine and the priest were both still asleep.

When she did not embark on the ship the next morning alerts were sounded among the Brotherhood to try to find her and bring her back into care. Senior Freemasons throughout the area and Europe were asked to look out for her.

We have since established that after leaving the lodgings she walked for a long time out into the countryside until, frightened and worn out, she found a farmer's barn and fell asleep in the hay. The farmer found her and the second night he and his wife, struck by her youth and beauty, gave her the best bed in the farmhouse in which to sleep.

The next day Felicia moved on as she believed she was too near to Hamburgh. The couple who gave her a bed for the night would take nothing from her for their trouble. Felicia got a ride in a carriage towards Sweden but three days into the journey she fell from the vehicle, suffering a dangerous wound to her head. She was taken to a nearby inn and a surgeon was called who attended to her injuries. She lay some days recovering from them.

A Dutch family, who stopped at the inn to break their journey to Sweden, took pity on her and paid for some of her treatment. She travelled on to Stockholm with them along with a Lutheran priest who was also travelling in that direction.

At Stockholm she found lodgings at the house of a German woman whose husband worked for the Government. By now she was worried that she would fall into poverty as the money in the blue purse was running out. She began to fear poverty more than the convent.

One day a hairdresser who was tending to her told her that the Imperial Minister of Stockholm, Count de Belgroso, was looking for a girl that had run away from Hamburgh. She told the hairdresser she was the girl and to let the Ambassador know. The Ambassador sent a note summoning her, which was read to her by a servant girl called Sophia and she immediately went to Count de Belgroso's house where she was questioned about her flight from Hamburgh.

Count de Belgroso, along with many other senior members of the Brotherhood in the area, had been asked to look out for her.

He told her he was instructed to take the greatest care of her, paid for her lodgings to date and arranged for her to move to the house of a Masonic tradesman. The Ambassador sent food and provisions for her.

A few days later he contacted her to say he had been instructed to protect her even more and she was moved to his own house to keep her safe. Here the Ambassador said she fainted when she saw a picture of her father, Francis I, hung on the wall. She could not be brought round for some time. Within days she fell ill with a fever, which lasted six weeks and left her weak and unstable in health. She is said to have grown taller during this time and her appearance altered so that she appeared to be closer to 30 years of age, although she was in fact still in her teenage years.

At this time the Ambassador became aware that another girl had gone missing in Hamburgh at the same time as Felicia.

This girl, the daughter of a merchant, had left the city in the company of an Englishman. He was asked by the Brotherhood to question the girl in his home to try to ascertain whether she was, indeed, Felicia or the other girl.

At first she told him that she had no English acquaintances at all but he persisted and questioned her again and again. Under pressure she falsely confessed that she had indeed left Hamburgh with an English gentleman and from this Count de Belgroso understandably believed her to be the merchant's daughter and not the daughter of the Emperor.

As a result of this he told her that he was mistaken in caring for her and advised her to return to Hamburgh. He gave her 25 Louis D'ors coins to cover her transport costs back to Hamburgh and sent her on her way with a merchant who was going that way.

Back in Hamburgh she looked for the priest and others and walked every day on the quayside and it was here she was spotted by one of the Brotherhood who had originally been in the party planning to take her to Bordeaux. He alerted other Brethren and arrangements were made to take her as planned by ship to France.

She was taken care of during the voyage and on arrival in Bordeaux she was taken to the house of the German Merchant for the first night and after that she went to meet Madame Guillaumont, who the Merchant had arranged for her to lodge with.

A week later a letter was sent to her by the Brotherhood addressed to Mademoiselle Felicia Juliana de Schonau. Madame Guillaumont read the letter to her. It set out the rules for her future conduct and assured her that she would receive ample money as a fund had been left by the Emperor for this purpose. She was advised to stay with Madame Guillaumont, who was asked to move out all her other boarders so that her secrecy could be maintained.

Some days after this a purse with one thousand Louis D'ors was delivered to her at the house and she was told not to enquire where the money had come from. It was the first payment from the money set aside by her father. With this money she was able to take a house and furnish it, with Madame Guillaumot as her companion.

Soon afterwards she received an anonymous letter in which she was commanded to go to the Duke de Richeleu. He told her he had received a letter from the Princess d'Auersberg asking him to look after her.

She attended many high society events that he organised. When people asked him who she was he would only say, "She is a lady of great distinction".

The Duke made overtures to her that were not always welcome. On one occasion he was said to have proposed marriage to her but she said she was bound to perpetual celibacy by the promise she had made to her father in Bohemia when he visited.

She also became friendly with a Counsellor of the Parliament of Bordeaux at the high society events she attended, and he also proposed to her, with the same result.

She continued to live in this way for some time, becoming known by people of the highest class in Bordeaux. Regular sums of money were brought to her, but she had never been told precisely who her father had been.

A total of 150,000 livres was delivered to her over time and this simply made her understand that she belonged to a very wealthy family. She spent the money as fast as she received it and lived a wealthy lifestyle. Then, suddenly, the payments stopped.

This was because Johann Karl Phillip, Graf von Cobenzl, was carrying out an audit of the money he was administering and could not find good reason among the papers as to why large amounts of money were being sent to Bordeaux on a regular basis. He stopped all payments - as he did with other payments - while he checked on everyone who was receiving money.

Felicia continued to live in the manner to which she was accustomed, unaware that no more money was to be forthcoming, and soon ran up debts of 60,000 livres. In debt and finding it difficult to make ends meet, she speculated on her parentage and in discussions with Madame Guillaumont, she came to the conclusion that her father must be the late Emperor. They also supposed that the person charged with ensuring she was furnished with money had died and that others did not know where she was residing.

Madame Guillaumont wrote letters on her behalf to some of the most illustrious people in Austria, who had been associated with the Emperor, in the hope that one of them might have been told about her by the Emperor. Felicia dictated some of these letters.

It is believed that one of these letters fell into the hands of her mother, Princess d'Auersperg, who asked the Duke of York to go to Bordeaux, find her and find out how much her debts were. The Duke met her at six in the morning, after a ball given by the Duke of Richelieu, when most people were sleeping. This was done in order to maintain as much secrecy as possible.

The Duke of York gave her 700 Louis D'Or and told her that he would soon ensure she had enough money to pay off her debts. He then left Bordeaux.

A few weeks later Felicia fell sick and a letter was brought to her from the Duke of York. The person who read the letter to her said that it was dated and headed from "Monaco". Only a short part was read before Felicia snatched it out of the hands of the reader as she feared it would reveal too much.

The wording of the letter, which is known was: "I was about to send you the remainder of your money; but when I left your house I received a letter, which positively commanded me to give you no more than a part of it. I have written to the Princess d'Auersperg and have requested permission at least to send you the sum you want to shelter you from the pursuits of your creditors."

Again with the help of Madame Guillaumont she wrote directly to Johann Karl Phillip, Graf von Cobenzl, asking if she could see him to explain her situation. Count von Cobenzl also had letters from other important people and Brotherhood members who knew of her fate, all urging him to take note of her.

In Brussels, Count von Cobenzl met Madame L'Englumee who had been in Bordeaux at many of the events held by Richelieu. She told the count that Felicia's features resembled the late Emperor; that she had her own house and was highly regarded by society there. This convinced him that she may be more than a pretender and he started writing to her.

Felicia had now been in Bordeaux for three years and a number of letters went backwards and forwards between herself and the Count de Cobenzl. She sent a portrait picture of herself, which the Count de Cobenzl showed to the Emperor's brother, Prince Charles, who felt that her features did resemble those of the family - although Count de Cobenzl was not so convinced.

She later sent the portraits she had been given by her father while a child, after asking a jeweller to remove the precious stones from the frames. Each letter sent by Felicia from Bordeaux intrigued the Count more, although in every letter Felicia was referred to simply as La Freulen. When the portraits arrived he could see they were of the Empress and Emperor and the Emperor's brother, Prince Charles, again recognised them as portraits by Liotard that he believed belonged to the family.

Letters continued between Count de Cobenzl and La Freulen and at one point he sent her a head-dress made of Brussels lace, but she wrote back saying she should return it to him.

Other letters, many unsigned, arrived with the Count telling him that he should support the young woman in Bordeaux. Whether these were genuine and a result of the letter writing campaign of Felicia or whether they were fraudulent and written by friends of Felicia in Bordeaux are unknown but the campaign gathered momentum and became the subject of gossip in certain quarters. Some members of the Brethren, concerned that the wishes of the Emperor would not be met, also wrote to the Count urging him to reinstate the sending of funds to France.

At the beginning of 1769 the Count received dispatches from Vienna saying that a requisition had been sent to Versailles for La Freulen to be arrested and to be taken to Brussels under a strong guard where she was to be questioned by Count de Cobenzl and the President Monsieur de Neny.

At the same time Prince Charles received a letter from the Empress, telling him to ensure that the young woman did not escape and to spare no expense in guarding her.

The letter from the Empress said, "This wretch wishes to pass for the daughter of our late royal master - if there was the least probability in the story, I would love her, and treat her

like any of my own children but I know that it is an imposture
and I wish every possible effort to be made that this unhappy
creature may no longer profane the dear and venerable name
of our departed Lord."

The Empress said that the arrest and questioning should
be made in the strictest secrecy and that there was already too
much noise about this matter and that if it was not dealt with
soon all over Europe would ring to it.

The Empress said she had heard about the woman in
Bordeaux through the King of Spain who had received a letter
purporting to be from the Emperor. This had proved to be a
forgery and he had sent news of it to the Empress to inform
her of the story.

Felicia was arrested and held in her own house in Bordeaux
in August 1769 by Monsieur Carel de Ferrand, a Lieutenant
of the Marchauseee of the Province of Gulenne, who was a
friend of the Empress.

News of her arrest spread fast, mostly among her debtors,
who now believing her to be a complete fraud, and realising
they would not get their money back, went to the house where
she was under arrest and made their views known. Even
Madame L'Englumee, who had given such a glowing report
to Count de Cobenzl, came to insult her. The words were so
brutal that Ferrand had to order her to leave.

Felicia suffered fear and distress and it is said she lost much
of her beauty. She had continual spasms in her stomach and
by the time they started the carriage journey to Brussels with
her as a prisoner she was spitting blood.

Her plight became known to the Brotherhood, who were
determined to still carry out the wishes of her noble father and
rescue her and protect her.

Because of her illness the carriage travelled very slowly to

Brussels and just before it left French soil a courier from the Brotherhood delivered a note to her through the coach window. It simply read: "My dear girl, everything has been attempted to save you; keep up your spirits, and do not despair." It was read to her by Monsieur de Poyot, an officer under de Ferrand who was travelling with her. She told him she did not know the person who handed her the note and did not know the hand-writing. On arrival at Brussels she was taken to the house of Count de Cobenzl for questioning.

The Questioning

The Count reported that she was dressed in a gown of grey taffeta, a black cloak and wore a veil of white gauze, which covered her face when she arrived. She was tall and elegant and her air simple and majestic. He said her complexion was fair; her arms delicately turned and her hair brown. He said she spoke French with a German accent and appeared confused.

She tried to kiss his hand but he prevented her by catching her in his arms. They had corresponded for so long that she addressed him by calling him "Father", something which she had started doing in the letters as he was her father's representative.

Count de Cobenzl talked to her about her health and said that she would receive kind treatment as long as she kept to the truth. She repeated many times:

"Yes my dear father, I will inform you of everything - I am a good girl, and never injured any human creature. It is true I have contracted some debts - but was that a crime? I had been plentifully supplied with money, and expected a continuation of my allowance."

The Count concluded that all her distress appeared

to come from the problem of the debts. She told him how distressed she was with the reaction of Madame L'Englumee and repeated a claim that she had made to Ferrand on the journey that Madame L'Englumee was inflating the value of the debt to her.

She appeared calm and asked if she might stay at Count de Cobenzl's house while being questioned but he told her she would be held at Fortress Monterel, just outside Brussels. She was transported there that night under the guard of Major de Camerlang and a female attendant.

The next day the Count went to see her at Fort Monterel, where she was in good spirits; she said she was delighted with the apartment she was living in and the conduct of those around her. The Count offered her the use of any of the books in his library and she said she did not have a moment to read - in reality she could neither read or write.

While she was in confinement Major de Camerlang taught her to sign her name. The following day her examination began. Count de Neny joined Count Cobenzl for the questioning and the first thing he noted was how striking her resemblance was to the late Emperor.

At the examination she was encouraged to tell of her earliest memories and all the twists and turns of her life to date. These are as related in the earlier part of this document. At no time did she claim to be the Emperor's daughter but her descriptions of the gentleman who came to see her and details of the pictures pointed at that fact.

She told her entire story up until arriving at Hamburgh when she then said she had boarded a boat to Brussels, missing out entirely the tale of her runaway. But under further and more severe questioning from Count Cobenzl, she broke down and, throwing herself at his feet, said that she had more to tell, but would no longer speak in front of Count de Neny.

Count de Neny left and Felicia asked for de Cobenzl to take pity on her and she said that all the details she had given up to the departure at Hamburgh were true. She then related the story of her flight to Sweden. She then gave great details of the people she mixed with while in Bordeaux at parties with Monsieur de Richelieu.

The letters that had been sent to Cobenzl about her were then presented to her. She admitted that she had dictated many of these when she was desperate and in debt while others she denied all knowledge of. She was told that forgery of this sort was a serious offence and her answer was that she had been desperate and that she had been led to believe that she was entitled to the money she had been sent.

One significant letter that she denied sending had arrived from Princess D'Auersberg to Richelieu asking him to look after Mademoiselle de Schonau. He had written back to the Princess talking about the girl, but had never received a reply from the Princess asking who the girl was, which seemed to indicate that this letter might be genuine and was strong evidence in favour of Felicia's story.

The examination of Felicia took place over 24 sittings over a number of days. During that time other letters were sent for and examined. At the end of the process Count de Cobenzl and Count de Neny met to decide what steps to take against the girl.

Their written verdict declared: "That the most prudent measure would be to place the poor girl in some distant convent, and there keep her, till time should throw some light on this mysterious affair." This opinion was about to be sent to Vienna to the Empress when a letter was received by Count de Neny from his father, who was private secretary to the Empress.

This said that the Empress, who had regularly been receiving reports of the proceedings, had formed a very disadvantageous opinion of the girl and that she was to be treated with the utmost severity. Believing it was what the Empress desired, De Neny proposed that Felicia should therefore be sent back to Bordeaux and put into the hands of her creditors, who should decide what should happen to her. He sent this to Vienna as his opinion.

Cobenzl did not agree and sent his own verdict to Vienna. He wrote the following:

"Though it appears to me that the prisoner is not the daughter of the Emperor, there are, however, circumstances in her story which throw a mysterious perplexity over her birth; and in this state of uncertainty, I cannot be of Monsieur de Neny's opinion.

"I likewise think that the measure proposed by that gentleman, of sending her back to her creditors, is repugnant to the well-known clemency and benevolence of her Imperial Majesty, and at the same time mitigates against her wish, that this affair should be buried in silence, as much as possible.

"If the poor wretch be sent to her creditors, she will be reduced to the fatal and horrible alternative of perishing without relief in a prison, or of seeking support in infamy itself, by means of her beauty and personal recommendations. And perhaps the Empress may be induced to pity this unfortunate young woman, when Her Majesty is assured that her morals appear to have been as yet irreproachable.

"Besides, to send her again to Bordeaux would be to give weight to those reports which ought to be suppressed - because all the world will say that, due to the imposture not having been punished, the story of her birth must needs have been in some measure believed. The objection, that it will be necessary to pay her debts, if we do not put her again in the hands of her creditors, appears to me trifling when compared with those serious evils, which will result from following my colleague's opinion.

"Her debts do not amount to 60,000 livres - she has effects of considerable value at Bordeaux, the sale of which will produce a great part of that sum; and the remainder appears to me below the consideration of Her Imperial Majesty's munificent heart. This generosity will give the Empress an absolute right to dispose of the unfortunate prisoner in such a manner as to rescue her from the dangers of seduction.

"My opinion therefore is: That Her Imperial Majesty send the stranger to a convent in the Tirol, or some other distant province of her dominions, where no rumour of the story hath hitherto been circulated. She may there pass a life of peace and obscurity at a trifling expense to the Empress. If time should throw any light on her history - if she should appear to belong to persons of rank and distinction, as the large sums put into her hands lead us to believe - we shall not have to reproach ourselves with those misfortunes to which this young creature will inevitably be exposed if M de Neny's advice should be taken.

"Indeed I look upon it as dangerous on every account. I should even prefer putting the prisoner to death at once, if this was not totally irreconcilable with every idea of the Imperial Majesty's clemency. If the court deign to listen to my opinion the young lady's property may be sold and her debts paid, without any suspicion on the part of her creditors that the Empress is concerned.

"And this they must not think, lest they should be led to suppose that Her Imperial Majesty is actuated by something more than mere pity.

"It will be sufficient to write, as from the stranger, to a banker at Bordeaux ordering him to sell her furniture and effects and to take an exact account of her debts. Whatever it may be necessary to add may be sent in the young lady's name - and her creditors satisfied with being paid, and having been accustomed to see her in possession of considerable sums, will have no reason to suppose the benevolent hand which affords this succour."

A diplomatic discussion then ensued for some time with Felicia held at Fortress Monterel for many months and into the winter of 1769 while discussions on the best course of action took place. The advice of Count de Cobenzl was not followed and it was felt impractical to carry out Count De Neny's recommendation. This was made harder when the Duke de Choiseul, Foreign Minister of France, refused to grant a passport for the return of the prisoner to Bordeaux.

An appeal to his decision was held, taking some weeks, but he persisted in his refusal of a passport.

In January 1770, Count de Cobenzl, at the age of 57, became gravely ill and subsequently died. The day before his death he said he had received dispatches from Vienna, saying more about the prisoner's history and that no action was to be taken until further instructions were received. The details of this were never clear.

Four days after his death, Felicia was packed up with all her belongings, including the three miniature portraits she had used as "proof" of her ancestry. She was given 50 Louis D'Or coins and was taken to Quievrang, a small town near Mons by a Sub-Lieutenant, and handed over to members of the Brotherhood. Locations had to be found to keep her away from those wishing her harm.

At first she was taken to Antwerp where she stayed in the

house of a trusted member of the Brotherhood. Here it was reported that she showed real signs of discomfort, sitting for long hours sobbing, wandering off in such a way that on two occasions a search had to be carried out and she was found sitting under a tree, apparently unsure where she was or what she was doing. It seems that the questioning had somehow shattered her fragile nerves, although a doctor who saw her said he believed she would fully recover in time.

It was impossible to take her to France because of the passport issue so her whereabouts was signalled to I, Thomas Dunckerley in England, who arranged for her to be brought by ship from Antwerp to England. This history has been given to your Lodge so you can fully understand the issues that this young lady has faced and her importance in Europe.

As the illegitimate sister of the Queen of France and daughter of Emperor Francis I, there is considerable political power associated with her that can be of great benefit to the Brotherhood. It is vital that she is kept safe from harm.

Because of the traumatic events of her life we believe she suffers from a number of distressing behaviours. She does not appear to now remember her past in detail. It has proved impossible to discern whether she chooses not to talk about events or whether she has genuinely lost that part of her mind.

Trauma during her flight from Hamburgh, including a serious head injury when she fell from the cart; further stress and mental fatigue as a result of her debts in Bordeaux; and more trauma on being arrested, and held prisoner from August 1769 to January 1770, have taken their toll on a young woman not yet 20-years-old.

As a result it is necessary at all times to ensure that she is kept in secure accommodation and that she is accompanied wherever possible. She is of a benign and happy nature but is not always logical in her decisions and behaviour and on a number of occasions has chosen to wander off and disappear.

Thomas Dunckerley
Grand Lodge 1770

OUT OF THE
HAYSTACK

- *Chapter One* -

Haystack Life

SNOW WAS FALLING steadily in Flax Bourton. Amy Atkings looked through the small window of her cottage and could see big flakes falling as silhouettes against a grey sky. The familiar fields and bushes of North Somerset had taken on a monochrome flatness.

The fire spat and roared in the grate, objecting to some sap still in the logs she had placed there earlier. The house was warm; thick walls and the constant tending of the fire had seen to that. William had not stirred yet, he was on his winter hours.

He spent longer in bed and in the house during the shorter days. There was little to do in the fields. Getting around in lanes thick with ice was difficult. He had learned years ago to rest up and wait. It would only be a matter of weeks before the days lengthened, planting was needed and it would be time to greet the year again with activity. February in Flax Bourton was an indoor time, living off the harvest of last year safely stored and preserved. That was how it worked in the countryside.

Amy was alone with her thoughts. It was hard to believe that it was now 1781. Another Christmas had passed by. She placed her hand on her own stomach. No sign of a baby to complete their family. She could despair if it wasn't for the encouragement of the women she knew. William would laugh if he found the box of charms she had hidden in her drawer.

There must be 20 or 30 of them now: one in the shape of a penis from some exotic country brought back by a sailor and passed to her quietly by Sarah Seymour, who swore it had worked for a friend; some crystals; stones and a pin brooch with a pineapple on it that had been given to Louisa and which she had passed to Amy saying sweetly that it was sure to help a baby appear.

She felt the resentment rise in her that Letitia Sparrow has fallen pregnant again so easily. The little girl was growing fast. Letitia had said that she wanted the little girl to be a free spirit so she had named her Louisa after the remarkable woman in the haystack.

The thought of Louisa made Amy look again out of the window. The haystack had completely disappeared into a white mass as snow covered everything. Louisa had now been living in the haystack for three years and Amy barely gave her a thought in the snow.

Whatever the weather Louisa seemed to survive, warm beneath layers of hay and blankets and clothing that well-wishers had brought. Gone were the days when they would rush down to check on her first thing if the weather was not right. Louisa would never take up an offer to come inside, seemed to just ignore the cold and the wet and simply seemed to survive somehow.

She heard William stirring upstairs. The sound of piss hitting the pot. The creaking boards. Amy found some tea and started to prepare for William to have a hot drink when he finally clunked down the short staircase and into the kitchen.

She put some of the tea into a tankard that stood on the side and snapped the lid shut. They would take it down to Louisa as soon as they had finished their breakfast. They knew she would be fine in the little grotto she had created for herself.

Others from the village would wander in turn down there later, probably with excited children keen to walk in the snow. Snow never lasted more than a few days in Flax Bourton and always caused great excitement among the generations who had not experienced it before and tales from the older people of longer winters, days and weeks when certain lanes were blocked, exaggerated stories of the height of drifts, length of icicles and temperatures that could freeze your breath.

Amy and William ate their morning porridge and drank their tea pretty much in silence before William observed, "It is not showing much sign of stopping and I would say there is around six inches on the fields and roads now."

"I expect the road is pretty well impossible to pass up through Barrow Gurney and the hill up to Downside was pretty well closed two days ago with the ice. With this on top of it there is no chance."

Amy picked up the tankard and a few other bits and pieces to take down to Louisa and, seeing what she was doing, William stirred and started to put on his boots. "I'll come down with you today to get an idea of how bad it is. It's still coming down really hard and it isn't going to thaw today that's for sure. I wouldn't want to be in the haystack in this weather but then I am not mad like our famous lodger."

Amy smiled. The constant string of visitors had only really slowed in the last few weeks. At Christmas there had been groups calling in while out on walks and several carriages had stopped with people in their finery stepping out and walking across to see Louisa. Many had left pieces of jewellery and small items, lots had left money and purses and bits of food.

Then there was the day just after Christmas when money and purses that had been given to Louisa turned up on the doorstep of all the women in the village that she knew. She had made a dawn perambulation of the village giving a little money to each household that she knew - returning the favours that they had given to her over the months and years of her time in the haystack.

Amy and William were now wearing the boots and coats and mufflers and hats that would protect them against the snowy day and pulled open the door only to see a small step of crisp white clean snow that had piled against it. William stepped over it and his feet scrunched on the fresh snow. Outside it wasn't as cold as they feared. There was hardly any wind and now large flakes were floating slowly down all around them.

"It does look lovely," said Amy, sticking her tongue out in a way that she had when she had first encountered snow as a child and turning her face up to let the flakes land on her. First stop was a look in on Jessie in her stable. She was stood unconcerned and William talked to her and patted her and put some feed into the trough, checking the water wasn't frozen, before turning back out into the winter air.

They trudged to the haystack, looking back occasionally at their footprint tracks and stopping to marvel at the sculptures the snow had made on the hedgerow. There was no sign of Louisa being present at all as they approached the haystack - just the incongruous nature of a haystack being there at all in the winter weather - a rough marine oilskin thrown over one side of it.

Amy called out but there was no reply, so she pulled back the oilskin to open up a small hole into where Louisa was crouched in the depths of the haystack, blankets around her, seemingly in suspended animation or dozing.

After a few seconds, which seemed to last a while, she smiled and acknowledged their presence and reached out her delicate long fingers towards Amy who put the tankard into her hand. Louisa flipped back the lid and crouched over the steam letting it play on her face before sipping the tea while cupping the tankard in her two hands.

William peered into the dark of the haystack over Amy's shoulder. It took a few seconds for his eyes, which had been blasted by the white snow, to get used to the darkness, but eventually Louisa came into focus and he could see she was smiling.

"Are you warm enough in there?" he asked.

"Yes, warm. I have sheepskin from the farmers and blankets and it is quite nice here," she said, pulling a piece of sheepskin into view for William and Amy to see.

Trinkets and messages and odd bits and pieces hung all around her head. This was the third winter that Louisa had been in the haystack.

Nobody in the village now offered her a bed for the night, although just about any of them would if she knocked on the door and asked. Louisa did occasionally knock on doors and would sometimes go inside a cottage, but usually she would stand in the kitchen and always she would head back to the haystack as soon as she could. She was never slow to take food, drink or other gifts offered to her - but anything she had left over she would often share with others in the village.

On these cold days Amy and William felt they had her to themselves once again. In the summer or whenever it was fine there was almost always someone at the haystack, who had come to see her. Often they were tourists who had heard about the strange lady who had now been sitting in a haystack for several years and who behaved in a most peculiar way.

Amy and William trudged back to their cottage. They saw Louisa pretty much every day so they didn't really notice day on day many changes in her. But, if they cast their minds back to the vivacious and beautiful girl that first arrived, it was possible for them to realise that living the way she was had started to take its toll.

She was more listless, and in the winter sometimes barely moved for days, huddled up to keep warm in the base of the haystack beneath the layers given to her by well-wishers and local villagers. Her hair, which she hardly washed in the winter, was now matted and tangled. In the summer the women of the village would comb and style it for her - but these winter months went on without much personal hygiene taking place.

Although she now spoke more words of English and her foreign accent now had a peculiar West Country addition - particularly on words with "R's" in them - she was often silent and moody when people she didn't take to were around. There had been three occasions when a doctor had been called to her. On each occasion she had recovered quickly - twice from stomach disorders and once from a cough that stayed persistently with her for weeks.

But Amy and William had discussed many times how

unhealthy it must be living the way she did.

The winter weather thawed and as February turned to March slowly the days got longer, there was a little warmth in the sun and Louisa ventured out, spreading the sheepskins and blankets out to air them and becoming more visible to the residents of Flax Bourton that passed near her.

It was in May of 1871 that Mary Turner, a cousin of William Turner, was out riding from Belmont when she came across a crowd gathered around a haystack and, taking the reins of her horse, walked across to see what was going on.

As she approached there was raucous laughter from a group of young men and she saw a woman leaping around in an odd fashion, seemingly showing off to the crowd. She stopped and watched and Louisa started running round and around the haystack, occasionally stopping to stare at the men in a crazy fashion, which only sent them into more paroxysms of laughter.

Some of the more boisterous men, upon seeing Mary approach, calmed down and nudged others and it seemed she had disturbed a strange piece of entertainment, that she wasn't entirely sure was wholesome.

While she was still watching a small group of farm women arrived and told the young lads in no uncertain terms that they had better move on. The men started throwing coins onto a blanket on the ground and Louisa was making exaggerated bows and lifting her skirts up in an unseemly manner. One man presented her with a spoon and she gave an exaggerated wiggle and hugged him, slightly too tight for decency.

The local women, now standing hands on hips or arms folded, watched as the men slowly made their way to horses they had tethered nearby and rode off in the direction of Bristol. Mary Turner quizzed the women about Louisa and they told her the story of how she had come to be there and how she had now been there more than three years.

Mary Turner went over to Louisa, who was busy gathering

up the coins and a few trinkets, which she started hanging up on stalks from the haystack, alongside the hundreds of others that adorned her outdoor home.

"Does she speak?" said Mary.

"Yes, she does," said Louisa, who then immediately started laughing in a maniacal way that was completely exaggerated and over the top for her little comment.

"Is this true you have been here for over three years? How do you survive?"

Amy Atkings had joined the other women and pushed through them to talk to the visiting lady in her finery. There had been many occasions when women and men of breeding had stopped by to see Louisa, and quite a few who, like Mary Turner, had happened upon her by accident. Amy was used to telling them the story.

"We all keep a look out for her here. The local women here all paid to buy the haystack for her."

"Wouldn't she be better off in a hospital?" asked Mary. "She seems seriously deranged."

At the mention of hospital Louisa stopped gathering up the coins and turned towards the newcomer.

"Terrible things happen in hospitals. I am happy here. This is where I live. No good comes from being indoors."

Amy interrupted, telling Mary, "They took her to St Peter's in Bristol once, but it didn't work out. She came back here. She does nobody any harm and, as I said, we all look out for her in case things get out of hand with some of the visitors she gets from the city."

Mary Turner still seemed concerned about Louisa.

"But look at her. She is clearly not right in the head and I wouldn't be surprised if she has lice. Her skin is not good. She is still quite a young woman but being outside all the time is taking its toll on her. You can't look after her forever."

"Maybe not forever," admitted Amy, "and you are right, she

has been getting a little worse this year. I think the harsh winter took its toll on her."

"You mean she slept out here through all the snow and bad weather that we had? Couldn't one of you have found her a bed for the night? Or let her sleep in a stable or on a floor? This is not the way to look after someone who has these problems. There are professional people now who can take care of lunatics. I have even heard that sometimes they can be cured and live a normal life after a few months of good treatment."

Amy and the other women looked a little sheepish at the accusation. Maybe they were starting to take Louisa for granted. Maybe they weren't doing the best for her.

Mary Turner told them she was the cousin of William Turner at Belmont and said she would mention Louisa to him. She went to sit with Louisa and gave her a brooch that she was wearing.

"Do you know the big house on along the road here? My cousin lives there. Why don't you come to visit us tomorrow and we can see if we can find you a new dress and maybe clean you up a little."

Louisa took a shine to the way that Mary Turner was talking to her and smiled at her.

"I would like that. I will come and visit the house and see you tomorrow. That would be good. We are neighbours," she said. Amy and the other women shook their heads and there was much laughter and smiling amongst them at the thought of Louisa taking up an invitation to visit Belmont.

Amy said to the others under her breath, not loud enough for Mary to hear, "I expect she will have High Tea and go for a walk in the woods for a little poetry reading."

"At least she won't be in any danger with William Turner," another woman whispered back and the whole group started cackling and snorting while trying to avoid eye contact with Mary Turner, who was still sat chatting to Louisa and holding her hand.

The village women drifted away, leaving Mary Turner and Louisa sat talking and exchanging pleasantries. Before she left, Mary Turner put some coins onto the blanket and helped Louisa pin the brooch she had given her onto her own dress. She noticed that although it was old and faded it was a quality garment, the like of which she had rarely seen outside of London society circles.

After saying her goodbyes she mounted her horse and made her way back to Belmont where, after stabling the horse, she went in to see her cousin William and told him about her encounter. She said how she had invited Louisa to visit, but said it was highly unlikely as she didn't seem to have the capacity to understand everything that was going on.

William Turner told her, "I had heard a story a few summers ago that there was a vagrant living in a haystack in Flax Bourton but I assumed it was a temporary thing and the traveller had moved on. I never realised it was a woman or that she had been there quite so long.

"What fun to have such a romantic soul on our doorstep. Someone who has cast out the traditional way of life for something so different."

"To be honest cousin," said Mary, "I think it is more a problem in her head than romanticism but you and your poetry-loving friends always seem to see the romance in everything. The reality of living in a haystack for so many years is not really one for the great romantics.

"Her skin is suffering, her hair is wild and I got the feeling that if I hadn't arrived when I did she could have been rather taken advantage of by the young men who were there. She is still a relatively young woman, but what future does she have living there? The local women admitted to me that they can't look after her forever. She will likely end up in a sad state. How does anyone end up in a place like that?"

"Yes," said William, "it's not a good place for a woman to be.

She is very vulnerable living there. I know that Hannah More has helped many people in similar circumstances and there are many friends who can help out. I'll take a walk down there at the weekend and have a look at her myself and see if there is anything that we can do to help."

Early the next morning William was having breakfast with Joe when he heard a commotion outside. Mary, who was walking in the garden, came running in to say that Louisa from the haystack was walking towards the house. They went to the door to see the slightly dishevelled figure in fine clothing on their doorstep, smiling from ear to ear.

She greeted Mary as an old friend and Mary introduced her as "Louisa". She stepped inside the kitchen and they asked her if she would like some milk.

Nobody at Belmont drank tea. One of William's peculiarities was that he gave two guineas a year to each of his servants for them not to drink tea. A servant was summoned now, and appeared wearing white gloves, to give the milk to Louisa, who drank it straight down.

William was looking straight at the girl. He had given many beggars jobs in his household and he had it in his mind that maybe this girl could work for him and have a better life. He asked her where she had come from before she had lived in Flax Bourton.

"I have lived many places," she said, "in many countries, but I like it here. The people are good to me and it is a nice place."

Just those few words, with their rather awkward accent, convinced William that Louisa was not English.

He thought he would try something. "Parlez vous Francais?", he asked and Louisa looked a little confused and worried and looked towards Mary.

He looked her straight in the eye. "Sprichst du Deutsch?" he asked.

Louisa looked terrified. Those words again. The same words

that had been spoken to her at the hospital. She put down the milk and started to shake.

William tried again. "Dist du in Bohmen geboren? Sprichst du Deutsch?"

Louisa started shaking, her lip trembling, and burst into tears. She grabbed hold of Mary and Mary told William to desist with his questioning as clearly the foreign languages were having an effect on the woman. Her behaviour was like that of a small child and, just like with a child, a few moments later Mary was able to distract her by showing her a small milk jug in the shape of a cow and she calmed down and seemed to have forgotten her tears of just a few moments before.

Louisa seemed more comfortable out of doors, so the two men, Mary, Louisa and Mary's sister, Susanna, went for a long walk around the grounds of Belmont. They stopped off at various points where William still had the boards nailed to trees with poems by Hannah More on them.

They climbed up the steep and rocky path through the trees to an area where the trees had been cut back and you could look out and see the sea and the islands of Steep Holm and Flat Holm way out in the sea in the distance. Louisa seemed genuinely excited as they all sat and looked at the view.

All of them struggled slightly up the next steep incline where William gathered them all around another board and recited the poem on it that Hannah had written there - it set out the satisfaction one gets when one surmounts a sharp pitch of path and gets to the top and how that is true about overcoming all the difficulties of life. It seemed appropriate to recite it to the poor unfortunate visitor and she seemed to appreciate it and stood up and applauded when William had finished.

Louisa had got the hang of the fun in the garden now and ran on ahead through the trees as the party strolled on and they found her sat cross-legged next to another board pinned to a tree near a rock, pointing at it. It was Mary's turn to read

"Inscription on a Beautiful Retreat Called Fairy Bower", making it as dramatic as possible for their over-enthusiastic visitor.

William asked Louisa if she would like to read one of the inscriptions but she just shook her head. Soon they came upon a little cottage and William opened it with a key that was kept under a stone nearby. It had a desk and writing material and he said it was the little folly where his friend Hannah More often came to write the poems that Louisa had heard during her walk.

In fact Hannah had not been to the cottage for some time. The death of her good friend David Garrick in London had sent her into one of her dramatic illnesses and for the last year or so she had been in London, looking after Garrick's widow, Eva Marie. Well, in reality they had been leaning on each other because Hannah was every bit as distressed as Eva Marie at David's death.

The Garricks had been married for 30 years but it had been as much the parties, the socialising and the friendships that had made up their life. Hannah had been a big part of that for the last few years, writing plays that Garrick put on at their theatre in London. She had left Bristol to go to his funeral and had never returned.

She wrote to William several times a week - and not just because it was his money that kept her in the fashionable lifestyle. She knew he was as sensitive as her - they had designed the garden walk between them. The letters told of her days with Eva Marie, how they would have breakfast together and then separate so they could each read, write and work from their own rooms.

At four they dined together and then they would sit quietly together, each reading a book. At six they had coffee. In the evening other fashionable women would often come to visit them and the conversation almost always turned to the theatre, what a loss it was without Garrick and how London society was no longer what it was. At ten at night they often had salad and fruit.

The two women had spent days, weeks and months sorting

through Garrick's papers and donating interesting things to the British Museum. Sometimes they did not see other people for days, so the letters to William were one way that Hannah kept in touch with the outside world.

William kept all of Hannah's letters and delivered them here to the cottage. He told Louisa about her and her life in London. Among the notes Hannah had sent was one saying she was enjoying the solitude as she did not have to "entertain dunces or be obliged to listen to them". He saw it now. That one had hurt him. He glanced at it and read that line again as Louisa flitted around the cottage admiring Hannah's things but demonstrating every ounce of being a dunce or a simpleton.

William told Louisa all about Hannah and promised her, "We will write to her in London and tell her about your plight. I'm sure that next time she is here she would love to see you. You can come up here and visit her and hear her read her poetry first-hand."

Louisa gave a little jig of delight. Joe decided this was the moment to tell his favourite story against his old friend William Turner.

"I must tell you Louisa about this incident in London with our good friend here." They all gathered around in the little cottage, William shaking his head in feigned opposition and the women who had heard it before, but enjoyed Joe's telling, settling down for the fun.

"As a swordsman and a boxer William may expect lesser men to give way to him when he is walking so that he can walk by the wall and they walk in the road. One day in London, a man walking the opposite way refused to give way to him and they started to jostle and argue. William had his sword but the other fellow had no sword so challenged him to a fight with fists.

"Our friend here in those days was very accomplished with his fists, so he takes off his wig, his coat and his sword and gave them to a bystander to hold and they set to work fighting with fists as a small crowd gathers.

"After a while someone in the crowd tells William here that the man he is fighting is Broughton the Bruiser - none other than John Broughton, once the Champion of all England at boxing. On that news William agrees that, as a champion, Broughton should indeed be respected and the two men shook hands and had the utmost respect for each other.

"But that's not the end of the story. William here then looks around only to find that the bystander has taken advantage of the cover of the crowd that had gathered to make off with his wig, coat and sword, never to be seen again!"

The whole party were laughing at the familiar funny story, which perfectly summed up not only William's slight pomposity but also showed his human side.

Still smiling, laughing and chatting the party headed back down the hill towards Belmont House where Mary and Susanna sorted out some food in a bag for Louisa and gave her a scarf and some costume jewellery that they had. The sun was setting over the Bristol Channel at Clevedon, turning the sky a magnificent red, as they waved their goodbyes to Lousia.

As Louisa wandered away slowly, basket in hand, turning back almost childlike every 20 or 30 yards to wave and shout goodbye once more, the cousins giggled. "With that sky and such a strange wandering character it is like something out of one of Hannah or Anne's poems," said Susanna.

It was a short walk to the haystack and Amy looked pleased to see Louisa as she approached. Although Louisa often wandered away from the haystack she could invariably be tracked down to one of the lanes nearby, picking blackberries or sloes in season, leaving little trinkets for the women she knew or simply wandering idly and singing. Amy had lost track of her for several hours as she had disappeared into the Belmont Estate.

At Belmont House two things were happening that were to change the fate of Louisa within the next few months. Mary

Turner was downstairs with a candle lit, composing a letter to Hannah More in London, describing their day and the curious story of the strange maid living in the haystack.

Upstairs, Joe and William were sat on the bed. Joe was reading through the document they had borrowed outlining "the secret narrative of the Emperor's daughter" while William studied his reaction. As Joe finished reading the last page and looked up from the document William spoke.

"Do you think Louisa who visited today could be her?" he asked.

"She could be," said Joe. "If so, why have the Lodge left her to sit in a haystack?"

- Chapter Two -

The Dinner Party

THE PORTRAIT OF David Garrick hung heavy over the chimney-piece at the Adelphi, London, and every guest at the table could not help but glance up at it. It was now almost two years since he had died but his presence was still felt. This was the first dinner party called by his widow Eva Marie, since his death.

She, and her companion Hannah More, had spent most of the year reading and grieving. Hannah was always on hand with a religious text or some piece from the Bible, to such an extent that Eva Marie now jokingly called her "The Chaplain". There had been times during the long months that they thought they would never rejoin the fashionable parties with the famous artists and artistes that David Garrick liked to mix with. But time had started to heal and a dinner party for eight with the closest people to David and Eva Marie was the way to test whether life could begin again.

Those dearest and closest friends would then be joined by a handful more in the evening for a soiree and maybe, just maybe, it would rekindle a light of joy once more. Certainly, the man in the portrait would want to see this happen. He had been all about life, music, entertainment and fun.

But it had been a tough time for Eva Marie. So many other personal friends of her husband had also died: James Harris, Topham Beauclerk, who had also lived at the Adelphi; and even Dr Ralph Schomberg, Garrick's personal friend and one of the doctors who attended his deathbed had himself passed away in the last 24 months.

It seemed for so many months to Eva Marie that the world was black and filled with death. But quiet months of healing sat with Hannah More; the closure of visiting the memorial erected in Westminster Abbey in her husband's honour; and the slow passing of time had led her to this.

There were two other ladies invited. The first was Elizabeth Boscowan, a close friend of both, who Hannah knew well from her home back in Bristol and Elizabeth's connection to the Beaufort Estate. Then there was plump Mrs Elizabeth Carter, well known as a learned and much-admired intellectual, who could always be relied upon to keep dinner party conversations stimulating.

To keep the numbers even, as was good etiquette, four men were invited and seated alternately around the table. The first was the poet and playwright Dr Samuel Johnson. He and Hannah had something of a mutual appreciation society going. She loved to flatter the older gentleman by reciting lines of his back at him, while he often returned the favour with a verse or two he had memorised of Hannah's latest work. He would be the big attraction at just about any dinner party in London.

He had been a good friend to David. He arrived in his gaudy coach, a huge vehicle with carved gilded wheels. Each panel on its sides was painted to represent the seasons. It stood outside attended by his valet, Francis Barber, a Jamaican former slave dressed in silver livery. The manservant, who had been brought to England by Lord Bathurst from a sugar plantation, was now well-known himself in London society and often waited at tables or took coats at events where Dr Johnson was the host.

Today his job was to sit outside in the coach guarding it and wait for his master to come out of the Adelphi so that he could accompany him home. Just the cheery presence of the coach outside, which Eva Marie and Hannah had ridden in many times in the past, seemed to light up the party and indicate to the world that the social life of Eva Marie was beginning again. Dr Johnson was the guest that all fashionable women of the time would want at their event.

James Boswell was the second man present, having arrived in the coach with Johnson. A Scottish lawyer, he was well-known on the social scene and when he visited London every year he was a constant companion of Dr Johnson. Everyone knew him well and Hannah More enjoyed the banter with him, although he did have a tendency to get louder and looser with his language the more he drank.

Then there was Dr Charles Burney. He, Garrick and all the other men present would often meet at The Club, an exclusive gentleman's dining room upstairs at The Turk's Head in Soho. Although a musician, he was tolerated by the writers because he had recently written books on his own travels seeking out music across Europe. Eva Marie appreciated him because he had often produced music for her husband's theatre, bringing plays to life.

Last, but not least, was Sir Joshua Reynolds. He had painted the portrait that hung over the chimney-piece. During a break in the eating he went to look at it - not to study the portrait itself but to read the Shakespeare quotation that was now inscribed underneath it.

Eva Marie went over to him. "Topham Beauclark chose that inscription to go under the portrait. He thought it was the perfect description of David. Now, of course, he is dead himself."

"Yes," said Sir Joshua, reading aloud the first words of the inscription: "A merrier man, within the limit of becoming mirth, I never spent an hour's talk with awl…. That is true enough and a fair tribute to Garrick." His West Country accent rolling the R's in the first few lines seemed to give it even deeper fondness to Eva Marie.

"I find it difficult to be merry and I must admit I look forward to death now."

They were interrupted by Boswell, with drink in hand, who said to them, "Just seeing that face on the wall, captured so well by you Joshua, cheers me up and is a signal that we should all enjoy life here while we can."

The meal, set out as it was on a table with the sunlight streaming in from a spring-like April day, could not have been more convivial. Everyone knew that their role was to cheer Mrs Garrick up and bring her back into the social life.

Lichfield Ale was served along with the food and Boswell, his Scottish accent becoming more pronounced with every glass, became quite loud, but entertaining - eventually proposing a series of toasts to each of the grand people present, including his good friend Dr Johnson, who some years before had long given up drink.

Johnson raised his glass of water and responded, saying, "Gentlemen, I wish you all as well as you do me." The fact that he had toasted using water and addressed the mixed crowd as gentlemen set people off giggling and that set the tone for the rest of the meal.

The chatter was of writing, particularly political, religious and philosophical writing. Mrs Carter and Dr Johnson fell into discussions about the writings of the Whig politician Thomas Hollis; Sir Joshua Reynolds and Mrs Boscowan were busy on the other side of the table discussing the pros and cons of the published sermons of Zachariah Mudge. Eva Marie loved the chatter and was enthusiastically joining in - somehow the buzz in the room seemed to bring back to life the feelings she felt when her husband had been alive.

After they had eaten they left the table and others arrived as the party went into the early evening. Boswell, now swaying on his feet, kept trying to persuade little groups to play the rhyming game Crambo - he was well known for his rhyming and wit and liked to be the centre of attention.

Most were gathered around Dr Johnson and a debate started about whether it was a dull life being a writer. Dr Johnson, giving examples of writers with interesting lives, talked about an author he knew who had married "a printer's devil". Sir Joshua Reynolds called out, "Sir! A Printer's Devil. Why, I thought that was a creature with a black face and dressed in rags."

Dr Johnson retorted, "Well, I suppose he washed her face

and put clean clothes on her." He then looked serious and said: "She did not disgrace him, she had a bottom of good sense".

Dr Johnson's use of the word "bottom" in this strange context sent everyone into fits of suppressed giggles, the women having to hide their faces at their embarrassment. Boswell chose that moment to slur in his Highland tones that a game of Crambo was about to begin and Mrs Garrick, Mrs Boscowan, Mrs Carter and the newer guests gathered around him to start the game.

It was at that point that Hannah More got into conversation with Sir Joshua Reynolds and Dr Johnson about their recent lives and pieces of writing. Hannah went to her room and retrieved the letter she had recently received from Mary Turner. She had particularly enjoyed a description that Mary had sent about a young woman that had visited Belmont and had enjoyed a day looking at the poetry trail there.

Sir Joshua had been to Belmont and had given some advice on planting and design to make the views. Dr Johnson was always keen to hear young Hannah's enthusiastic view of literature. It was through her that he had heard about the work of the young boy Thomas Chatterton who had committed suicide in Bristol. They both now believed he was a genius of literature and wanted to ensure his name became known.

Hannah read the relevant paragraphs from the letter. They painted a romantic picture of a free spirit living in a haystack. Her joyous simplicity at enjoying the poetry and scenery at Belmont and finally her retreat into the sunset. It was all described in such fantastic detail that all of them agreed this was a marvellous subject for literature or indeed painting.

"I intend to go to see the Maid of the Haystack next time I am back in Somerset," said Hannah. "She would be an amazing subject for your painting, Sir Joshua. From all the descriptions she is absolutely beautiful."

"I'm not likely to get down to Bristol soon," said the great painter. "But I have a rather keen young Irish pupil William

Palmer. He is badgering me for subjects at the moment. I think it would be great experience for him to travel down to Bristol. He wants subjects to paint so that he can submit them to exhibitions.

"I'll pay for him to come to Bristol. He's a young lad. If she is a beauty then what could be better? You never know she might be persuaded to leave the haystack with him. He has that Irish charm!"

The deal was sealed but Hannah was also concerned about the well-being of the young lady and the fact that Mary had made it clear that the woman was unable to read.

Dr Johnson said, "I feel this may end up being be another of your projects Hannah. You were always so enthusiastic about the education of women. I have never had such an exciting time than when I came down to Bristol to see you and your sisters determined to teach other women to read and write.

"The progress those waifs and strays made was remarkable and many were a match for any man by the time they had learned from you and your sisters."

Hannah spoke, "Seriously, I do wonder about the mind of a woman who will sit in a haystack for so long. She is in a dangerous place there. People think the countryside is benign compared to the city but I can tell you there are footpads, chancers and evil men stalking the lanes of Somerset just as much as in the grimy lanes here in London.

"Imagine, all that time in all winds and weathers. No walls to hide behind in safety. Relying on others to bring you food and clothing. It must be absolutely awful for the poor thing. Yet, nobody does anything about it or seems to care. It sounds romantic but the reality is something completely different."

The two older, learned men looked slightly chastened. This was what they liked about Hannah and why they liked to spend time in her company. Her passion and different view of the world was always stimulating and exciting.

"We haven't seen enough of that passion in you in the last

year or so since David died," said Dr Johnson. "Just because one person has died it does not mean the rest of us must die with him. The best way we can honour David's memory is to live happily and enjoy the days we have - and in your case do the deeds that are so important to you."

With that a peel of laughter came from the group across the room playing Crambo. It was Eva Marie; a few drinks inside her, she had suddenly taken on the old character they had known.

Boswell had made up a rhyme about the musician Burney and as a consequence Eva Marie, had grabbed Burney and was pleading with him to play the harpsichord that sat idle in the corner of the room. At first Charles Burney feigned reluctance but then he sat down and began to play beautifully, shouting over to Eva Marie, "If I have got to play then you have got to dance."

It was a beautiful and lilting, haunting tune and Eva Marie, began to sway to the music and did eventually start a little dance on her own. The assembled were touched by the significance of Garrick's widow suddenly being so joyous - even though they knew it was partly fuelled by the drink.

Suddenly Eva Marie shouted to the assembled, her German accent now quite strong, "Take your partners for a dance," and all assembled paired up, apart from the observing group of Hannah More, Reynolds and Dr Johnson.

Dr Johnson turned to Hannah and observed, "She is a remarkable lady in that, although the finest women come to check with her that they look good, you never notice what she is wearing. She is so good at it."

"Yes," said Hannah. "Even though I am with her every day her foreign accent and the way that she does not pronounce the letter "t" properly still charms me. I have rarely seen her dance even though she was a top dancer across the whole of Europe in her day."

"Ah yes I have heard the story," said Dr Johnson. "They called her La Violette. It was a stage name given to her by Empress

Marie Theresa when she danced in Vienna. They say that she was sent to England by the Empress because the Emperor was giving the young dancer too much attention. Here, in London, the Earl of Burlington and his family took her under their wing.

"I first saw her with Garrick in Drury Lane. Lady Burlington used to wait at the side of the stage with a pelisse to wrap around her when she came offstage. She was an incredible dancer and a beautiful thing. You could see why David fell for her - and they were devoted to each other."

The party broke up while it was still light and Eva Marie was laughing and shouting at the door as each of the guests left. Boswell and Dr Johnson left together. Boswell was a little unsteady on his feet so Dr Johnson signalled to his manservant Francis that they would be a moment and they went over to the rail overlooking the Thames so that Boswell could get some air in his lungs.

Boswell said, "I don't think I can ever remember having a better time. What a magnificent party. I always have such a good time here in London with you. We have a few more things to look forward to yet."

"Yes," said Dr Johnson. "It has been a good evening. It was also good to see you enjoying the Masonic dinner. In your new position as Deputy Master of the Grand Lodge of Scotland I think you cut quite a dash and were in great demand that night. We have had some lively evenings this last month or so. Maybe not as lively as some of our evenings touring the Hebrides but the best you might find in London."

Boswell drunkenly put a hand on his old friend's shoulder. "The best time with you, my friend, as always, is when we have our traditional evening at The Mitre, the pub we first met. I always look forward to those evenings when I am down here. I need my regular dose of London. Scotland is far too dreary at times."

The men fell quiet and looked at the Thames.

Boswell broke the silence. "I'm thinking about two good friends who lived in that building behind us who we have now lost and who won't be joining in the fun, Beauclerk and Garrick."

Dr Johnson looked rueful and sad and replied tenderly, "Ay sir, two such friends as cannot be supplied".

- Chapter Three -

The Painting

AMY ATKINGS WAS a little surprised to find someone in such finery
as Mary Turner on the doorstep of her modest cottage, asking to
come in. She was suddenly aware of how small the place was and
how completely full of things it was, mostly items that William had
brought home at some time.

But Mary seemed quite insistent and said she needed to chat
about Louisa. It meant quickly moving clothes and objects as
Mary followed her into the dimly lit room, taking some washing
off a chair and inviting the lady to sit down.

"What is it about Louisa?" asked Amy, not sure whether
offering a cup of tea would be appropriate, while worrying that
she did not have any decent cups to serve it in.

"I understand you look after her and I have some people that
I want to bring to see her today," said Mary.

"I don't look after her. I just look out for her. People visit her
all the time and she is free to do what she likes. I just try to make
sure that things don't get out of hand down there at the haystack.
Some of the local lads take a few liberties."

Mary smiled and changed her tone a little. "I suppose I am
asking for your help. I'm sure you have heard of Hannah More.
She is a good friend and she has sent a portrait painter from
London who is coming here today. The painter wants to set up
an easel and paint Louisa's picture."

Amy smiled. She was used to people from the city and the
Hot Well and society folk calling in to see Louisa. Now it was
May and the weather was getting better she expected the visits to
start again. Thankfully, most left some money for Louisa and that
was how she survived. There were times in the summer when
Louisa seemed to earn more just sitting and dancing around a
haystack for the amusement of the upper classes than William

did working all day. She decided to lay it on a little thick.

"A portrait painter! That's a new one," she said, "Just knock for me and I will walk down with you. I'm sure Louisa will love the attention. It is getting more and more difficult for her. She has been sat in the haystack now through three winters. She never comes inside. The only money she has to buy food or anything else is what people leave for her."

Mary smiled. "Yes, I know. When she came to Belmont a while ago, she was good company, if a little eccentric, but I can't imagine what it must be like living as she does every day. I've spoken to Hannah More and her sisters and Hannah is intending to come to see her when she is next back in Bristol. She has a house now in Sandford so passes along the road here and she says she will stop by."

The two women chatted for a while and Amy told her how Louisa now sometimes seemed weary and had lost some of her spark in the colder winter days. There was no doubt that her lifestyle was taking its toll on her.

After a few moments they made arrangements for Mary to knock on the door later when Amy would be ready to take her to see Louisa.

It was two hours later that the knock came and Amy fell into step with Mary and the painter, William Palmer, and they made their way across the fields. Mary was carrying a small box with the paint and paintbrushes belonging to the young artist. He was a pleasant enough young lad with a strong Irish accent, carrying a wooden folded easel with a handle in one hand and a roll of canvas in the other.

As they neared the haystack they saw Louisa skipping around in a long dress to the amusement of a small group of men nearby. They were shouting ribald comments at her and she appeared to be pulling down the top of her dress to show her cleavage to them. As they saw the two women and the artist arriving, the men stood up and made off in the opposite direction, each throwing a coin into a small basket that was in front of the haystack as they left.

Louisa was looking in the basket and arranging the coins into a long row on the ground in front of her as the trio arrived. She smiled at Amy and Mary and looked curiously at William Palmer who was already busy setting up the strange contraption of his easel.

Palmer spoke to her. "Pleased to meet you Louisa. I have heard so much about you. You can relax for a while. I'll be a wee few minutes getting things ready."

The women sat down and Amy produced some cups and some milk from a bag she was carrying and poured one for each of them. Louisa took it and drank heartily, while Mary toyed with her cup and William placed his on a stone nearby, taking several tries to get it straight, before wandering around the haystack looking at it from all sides. Amy also unwrapped some apples that had been carefully stored since the previous autumn and gave them one each as a treat.

"How have you been?" said Mary to Louisa.

"I am fine. The weather is good now."

Louisa's hair, which stretched down over her shoulders, looked a little wind-blown and her face was thin and pale, but she had survived the winter in good heart. To the people living nearby it was no longer remarkable that a woman was living in the haystack at all. She was just part of the local scene.

Palmer pinned his canvas to the easel and prepared his pencils and paints and then called the women around. In his soft Irish accent he explained where he wanted Louisa to sit and told them that he wanted a view into the distance where there was a gate through which most people entered the field.

Louisa started pulling down the front of her dress and William found a long piece of material amongst her belongings and the women helped to arrange it around her shoulders. Her left hand held the cloth against her bosom and her right hand he asked her to outstretch upwards as if she was asking for money.

He put the basket alongside her and for good measure arranged the apple he had been given next to it. The young artist was swift with his pencil and kept up a constant stream of chatter with the women as he drew and occasionally filled in small areas with his paintbrush.

"So, what part of Ireland are you from?" asked Amy.

"I come from Limerick originally. My father is a draper there. I've been studying art in Dublin and fairly recently went to London to study with Joshua Reynolds. There are a few of us there. He really is a genius but we can pretty much do whatever we want. He lets us copy things and you can learn a lot just from watching him.

"I need to build up a portfolio, you see, and I'm looking to have a good male portrait and a good female portrait to help me make my name. I hope one day to set up my own portrait painting practice."

Louisa sat relatively still throughout the process, although her hand drooped downwards in time. Two men stopped by the gate and chatted for a while and Palmer sketched them and did a little drawing on some more paper of the trees and haystack around.

After he had finished his work he showed it to Louisa, who seemed impressed and beckoned for him to come close to him at the haystack. From deep within the haystack she brought out the three portraits that she had to show him.

"These are very high quality," said Palmer. "Who are these people? They have very fine clothes. Are they European?"

"This is my Mama and this is my father and this one is the Queen," said Louisa without hesitation.

"Where were these painted?" asked Palmer.

"In Bohemia, I believe. My father gave them to me. It is all I have of my family." Louisa looked slightly upset and the Irishman changed the subject and jollied her along with a little flattery about how well she had sat for the session. As the little group left, Louisa was quietly wrapping the portraits carefully once again in their blue bag and hiding them in the depths of the haystack.

It was only a 10 minute walk to Belmont. Within a few moments Mary and William Palmer were knocking on the door of the house. They took off their muddy shoes at the entrance and went inside where William Turner and Joe had arranged for the staff to prepare a little supper for them. The artist Palmer showed William Turner and Joe the sketches he had made and told them how he intended to flesh the painting out once he got back into the studio.

"She's actually a really nice girl," said Palmer. "Far different to how I thought she would be. She sat quite still for the portrait. She even showed me some fine portraits she has herself of her own family, clearly painted by an excellent portrait artist. Superb miniatures."

William Turner and Joe looked at each other and quizzed the portrait painter more about what he had seen.

He described each of the portraits in detail; one showing a man; one showing a woman and a third showing a veiled woman. William and Joe realised as he spoke that these clearly matched the portraits described in the secret document they had read.

Nothing was said to Palmer but the two men decided to act the next day and to go to the Masonic Lodge and explain what they had discovered - they were convinced that Louisa must be Felicia - the illegitimate daughter of the Emperor and sister of the famous Queen of France. It was extraordinary that she should be sitting in a haystack a few yards from their home in Somerset, England.

It was, of course, the younger Thomas Dunckerley that the two men met in a quiet room at the back of the Masonic Lodge in Bristol the next day. Joe had the papers they had borrowed in a bag and, after some pleasantries, handed them back to be returned to the safe. All except the manuscript entitled "A Secret Narrative of The Emperor's Daughter" which he kept in his hand.

Young Thomas was busy packing some clay pipes with tobacco to hand around and, acknowledging the papers put on the table, he asked the young men, "Thank you. I'll return them to the safe. Did you enjoy them?"

"Very much," said Joe. "But this one is not an erotic story. It is a document about a girl that has been put into safe keeping with our Brotherhood. It tells the story of the illegitimate child of Emperor Francis I and how your father was charged with keeping her safe - and we have good reason to believe she is living in a haystack near our home. Have you heard about the Maid of The Haystack?"

Young Dunckerley looked concerned and held out his hand for the paperwork. "Let me see. I didn't know that was amongst those papers. You probably shouldn't have seen it! I do know about the Maid of The Haystack and some time ago she was taken into hospital as my father suspected she might well be the Emperor's daughter. But a doctor examined her and my father had people look through her things and they came to the conclusion that it is not her.

"Felicia, who is mentioned in this document, disappeared without a trace some three or four years ago. It was a delicate matter for the Lodge. But with the Emperor dead and nobody knowing anything about her, it was never pursued. I believe the girl in the haystack is just a travelling person, probably from Europe, but nobody knows for sure."

Joe and William lit their pipes and smoke began to fill the small dingy room, that was getting increasingly grey by the moment as light was fading outside.

William spoke, "In this narrative it talks about Felicia being given portraits by the Emperor and that she carried them with her. A portrait painter came down from London last week at the behest of Hannah More and he says she showed him portraits that sound exactly like those in this story."

Thomas Dunckerley remained unconvinced.

"There is no real interest in this now. The Lodge felt that it discharged its duties. We were told that this girl was coming to Bristol to see my father but she never arrived.

"My father spends most of his time in Hampshire at the moment, where he is forming a new Lodge, and in Hampton Court with the Royal Family. He is accepted now, unofficially, as a member of the family and there is a plan to have a Hampton Court Lodge in due course. His interest in the legacy of the Emperor wained some time ago. They were good friends in their day."

William spoke up, "I'm convinced this is her. There is just such an uncanny connection between Felicia in the story and the girl in the haystack. The fact she arrived just at the time you were expecting a princess from Bohemia is just too much of a coincidence.

"She is far from stupid. She came to my garden and understood poetry. She acts strangely but it would be a huge scandal if it comes out that she was entrusted to the care of the Masonic Order and fell into a life like this. This girl can't live in a haystack forever.

"My friend Hannah More has been involved in setting up enlightened places that can house lunatics and those with unsound minds. Whether she is a princess or a beggar I think we should find her a better place to stay and Hannah will know what to do."

Young Dunckerley nodded in agreement. "Maybe you are right. I'm sure Miss More will be able to help. We don't want any scandal reflecting back on us."

He turned to the papers they had brought in. "I'll put these stories back into the safe. I bet it was a real disappointment when you got to this one," he said, waving the Narrative of the Princess.

The two friends laughed and the conversation moved on to other matters.

Chapter Four

Henderson's Madhouse

THE DINNER PARTY seemed to reset life for both Eva Marie and Hannah More. Both started back into society once again and Hannah was pleased to go to see Joshua Reynolds in his London studio and to meet the young artist who had travelled to Bristol to capture an image of the Maid of The Haystack.

The studio was well-lit and an overwhelming sensation came from the smell of the oils. A number of students were in the room but William Palmer stood pleased with himself in one corner. He had carefully positioned two canvases for Hannah More to view, aware that she had been his sponsor for both these projects enabling him to get his wish of a male and a female portrait of some interest to put into exhibitions.

Hannah viewed the portrait of John Henderson first, as he was a young lad she knew well. His father, Richard Henderson, ran the school in Hanham, set up by celebrated preacher John Wesley, that her sisters and herself had taught at and which they had helped to fund by finding rich people willing to help out with their educational projects.

Palmer had captured John Henderson at his desk in Pembroke College, Oxford. Although incredibly clever, speaking many languages, including Greek and Latin, he still looked like a boy. Palmer's portrait of him leaning on a thick book surrounded by shelves of other learned books delighted Hannah.

"That is incredible. It's so much like John. He used to assist with the teaching at his father's school. He was teaching Latin at the age of eight to other children. You have really captured his scholarly nature there. The likeness is uncanny. It is as if he is in the room."

"I am so glad you like it," said Palmer. "We got on very well. He and his father are from the same place in Ireland as me - Limerick - although he doesn't remember much about the homeland as he moved to Bristol with his parents at a very early age. But he says he would like to go back there some day and if he does I'll be sure to meet up with him and show him around. We are corresponding."

Hannah More clapped her hands in delight. "It really is special. I believe he will take after his father, who is one of the most favoured speakers by John Wesley on Methodism. I intend to go back to Bristol soon and I will tell Richard that he really must come to see such a fantastic portrait of his son."

William turned to the next canvas, which he had covered with a cloth as Hannah had entered. He now lifted the cloth for dramatic effect and revealed the Maid of The Haystack.

"Oh she is beautiful, and if this likeness is half as good as the one of John then I can see why she is talked about so much. The colours look so much like my beloved Somerset. It really is striking."

William said, "Yes, I was keen to get some detail into the hay and leaves and her wild hair. She really is a forlorn figure in many ways. She has been living there for four years now. She is harmless but clearly quite mad. She showed me some superb portraits someone had given her and said they were her own family, although to be honest they looked like noble people from the continent."

Hannah studied the picture and a tear formed in her eye. The bare foot sticking from under Louisa's dress, the odd expression that was both forlorn and pleasant at the same time. The outstretched hand begging for money. She looked deeper into the picture and saw two dandies standing by a gate chatting.

"She is so vulnerable there with men passing by. She appears to just have a piece of cloth of some kind that she is gripping to her bosom."

"Yes," said William, looking down slightly embarrassed, "when I got there men were teasing her and I had to get her to cover up for the portrait. The local people look after her as best they can but there is no doubt that she needs proper care. The wind and weather is making its mark on her. Not surprising, I suppose, she has been through three winters outside in that haystack. I don't think I could endure it."

Hannah vowed at that moment that she would find a way to support Louisa. She knew that with many schools now springing up to support the poor in Bristol that Richard Henderson was looking at the idea of turning the building in Hanham into an asylum that treated lunatics in the new and more caring way.

Most asylums simply locked people up and kept them contained. His idea was that by keeping them occupied with religious teaching, accompanied walks and with useful things to do, there was more likely to be a positive response from them and maybe some could eventually be cured and move back into society.

By having a small number of people in a house in a nice location they could be treated in a medical way - after all the brain was an organ of the body like anything else and if it could be treated then people could be healed.

Hannah More spent an interesting few hours with Joshua Reynolds and met a few other pupils before setting off in a carriage to re-join Mrs Garrick. That night she wrote back to William Turner telling him about her viewing of the portrait and saying she agreed with his assessment that Louisa needed to be found a safer refuge and asking him if he was willing to divert some of the money that they used for other purposes into the care of Louisa if she could get her into the care of Mr Henderson.

It was a month or so later, and a bright sunny day in North Somerset, when Hannah More went to see her former suitor at Belmont, accompanied by Eva Garrick, who had come down to Bristol to spend some time in the countryside. They set off to walk from the house to go to see the "Maid of the Haystack" that they had heard so much about.

Hannah and Eva chatted as they walked together down the lanes, with William sometimes walking behind, sometimes alongside joining in the chatter. As they neared the haystack they saw that Amy Atkings and the women of the village were sat around chatting, sewing and preparing vegetables in a group.

For the last hour Louisa had been pacing up and down near the haystack. Her feet were bare, her hair a tangled mess and she was coughing badly. Sometimes she stopped her pacing for a moment to cough deeply from her lungs, bringing up phlegm into her mouth which she then spat upon the ground.

It was the first sight that Hannah More had of the figure that had been described so romantically to her. The reality of her four-year vigil in the haystack was clearly taking its toll but the women sitting around did not seem to notice Louisa's odd behaviour or care much about her. They were simply getting on with their own lives.

As Hannah, Eva and Turner approached together the women looked significantly at each other. All of them knew the story of how Turner and Hannah had been betrothed three times and yet never married. All of them knew that the man from Belmont now paid to keep this famous lady in the lovely clothes and the London society in which she mixed. They were all curious to see the pair together and taking an interest in the local village eccentric.

Amy stood up and did a little curtsy bob as the group arrived.

"Mr Turner," she nodded. "Miss More?" she asked; although she was certain she knew who the visitor was they had never met before. Hannah nodded and smiled. She was used to the attention and fame. After all she was a playwright, author, poet and well-known by the poor in the area for her schooling and support of women.

Hannah smiled. "This is my friend Eva Garrick. So this is Louisa?" she asked. "I have heard so much about her. She looks just like the portrait that was painted. I hear she has become something of an attraction around here with people coming out from Bristol for the day to see her. But what a dreadful cough! Clearly she is not well. Has she been like this long?"

"I believe it is just a cold," said Amy, "but there is less and less interest in her. She makes her money from the gentry who visit the Hot Well in the summer and a few other passing folk. The rest of the time we look after her as best we can. She just won't contemplate going indoors, but in all honesty I don't know how much longer she can live in the way she does."

Hannah nodded her head. "Oh, she is interesting enough and still young and handsome, but I understand can't throw any light on the mystery of her secret origin." Hannah and Eva sat down with the ladies. Louisa hardly acknowledged William Turner or the fine women that had arrived with him. William went close to her and looked her significantly in the eye and said: "Hello Louisa."

She turned away and coughed once more. Hannah sat with the small group of Flax Bourton villagers called over to Louisa who immediately stopped her pacing and coughing and dutifully came over to sit between Hannah and Amy. Suddenly she was beaming up at Turner and seemed to recognise him at last.

He spoke to her again. "Do you remember the poems that we read while we were walking around the grounds of my house?" Louisa nodded. "Well this is the lady I told you about who wrote them - Hannah More."

Louisa looked genuinely excited and surprised and, much to Hannah's surprise, and the amusement of the other women, hugged Hannah in an excited way, just as a child might hug their grandparent. The childlike move certainly endeared Louisa to Hannah, who took a comb out of a small bag she was carrying and, beckoning Louisa to move her head near, began running it through the tangled strands of Louisa's hair.

"Thank you," said Louisa. The combing was something Hannah felt comfortable and familiar with as she and her sisters had often helped each other in this way and whiled away many hours chatting and tidying their hair. Louisa certainly needed the combing and Hannah picked small pieces of hay out as she progressed.

After a few moments Louisa started coughing again and Hannah asked her how long she had been coughing like that and whether she needed anything to help cure it. Louisa was saying very little but seemed in a little distress trying to stop the cough. Hannah wasn't sure whether it was the coughing that was causing her to be so silent or whether her silence was part of her mental condition.

"You have been here for many years. I know you do not like the idea of being indoors but you need to rest in a proper bed and to get well. If I can arrange for a nice place with a garden where you can go outside and walk and see the countryside would you be happy to move there?"

There was something about the famous lady playing with her hair that calmed Louisa. Or maybe, after four years, she had finally had enough of living the eccentric life in a haystack. Amy was surprised to hear Louisa speak.

"Yes, I think I would like that. I like it here. The people are kind. But I need to get well and the wind and weather are not good for me. You are both very kind," she said, looking up at Mr Turner.

Eva Marie had been looking at Louisa curiously. There was something so familiar about the features of her face but she could not place it. Hannah and Eva sat with Louisa for around an hour and then took their leave with Turner to go back to Belmont. Later that night Hannah and Eva Marie went to Hannah's home at Barley Wood in North Somerset, which was being prepared for a special visit of other friends from London.

Turner had already said that he would contribute to some of the expenses of giving Louisa a new life at the Henderson's asylum.

Eva and Hannah chatted about what they might do with Louisa, Hannah describing her as "an unfortunate and inexplicable creature". The visitors to Barley Wood the next day were Lady Bathurst and her four daughters who had come down from London.

Hannah called the group "Lady Bathurst and her fair train". The Bathurst sisters reminded her so much of her own family. They were all independent and unmarried and were great friends. Hannah had become friends with Lord and Lady Bathurst and their family during her time in London and had frequently been to dinner parties at Apsley House. She loved being able to entertain them in Somerset, show them the countryside and tell them the ways of the rural community.

Of course the story of the Maid of the Haystack was told and Lady Bathurst immediately said she would also provide regular payments to help the poor soul recover. She knew Richard Henderson and his son John and was sure that the asylum would do wonderful work in supporting the poor unfortunate soul.

With that meeting in Barley Wood the future of Louisa was sealed. Hannah was able to go to see Henderson with her sisters the following week to explain that she had a person in need of the help and support that he aimed to give and on whom he could practice his new style of support for those in such conditions. She also had funding guaranteed for her care from reliable and trustworthy people.

For Henderson it was a wonderful opportunity as the Maid of the Haystack had a certain amount of fame and notoriety by now and knowing that such a well-known and fabled lunatic was living at the asylum might well prompt others to bring less fortunate members of their family into his care.

Of course he wanted to help people but he also had to make sure that the hospital he was creating was properly financed and able to clothe, feed and find worthwhile things for those living there to do.

He put an advertisement in Bonner and Middleton's Bristol Journal to announce his new venture. It read: "The public are hereby informed, that R Henderson, late Master of Hanham Academy, has opened a Receptacle for that most pitiable Class of the Afflicted - The disordered in Mind. There the patients will be carefully kept, well used, and every way compassionately attended to. Moreover every assistance in reach shall be employed for their care. The House will be visited by a regular Physician.

"This undertaking will be conducted at Hanham, near Bristol, on the upper Bath Road; where Particulars my be enquired, and legal and honourable Proposals be properly agreed on.

"NB: The Apartments are now prepared and some Patients received."

Hannah took less than a week to secure all the arrangements to finance Henderson taking Louisa in and she stopped at the Atkings' cottage on her way past early one evening and walked down to tell Louisa that soon she would be able to move to her new home. Louisa seemed resigned and happy about the move.

It was a poignant scene the day that Louisa left the haystack she had been living in for over four years.

For the last hour of her occupation Amy and William Atkings went to the haystack and sat with her for one last time. She was ill, forlorn and feeble compared to the vital and exciting person who had taken up residence there so many years before. They helped her put all her belongings, which consisted of a few rags of clothes and trinkets, coins, charms and cheap jewellery she had been given by well-wishers, into bags.

Amy held on to Louisa's hands. "It is just the other side of Bristol and we will come and see you next week. Miss More is a wonderful lady and you need to get well. Maybe when you are better you can come back here and see us again."

Louisa nodded unconvincingly. "I would like that," she said before coughing uncontrollably once again for a few minutes.

Amy took something out of her apron. It was the small bell

that William had brought home on the day that Louisa had appeared. She had always associated it with Louisa and now she gave it to her as a going away gift.

"Take this and whenever you need anything ring the bell and I am sure that it will come to you."

Louisa reached into the hay behind her back. She pulled out the three portraits still wrapped in their blue bag. She handed them to Amy.

"And you have these. You have been so kind. They are the only things I have from a life long ago. The people in the pictures are important. They will help you if you ever need anything. They can't help me now."

A carriage arrived at the allotted time with Henderson and Hannah More on board and they quietly and calmly took Louisa by the hand and led her across the field to the farm gate, Most of the village women had come along to say their goodbyes. They each went up to Louisa, giving her a loaf of bread, or cheese, some coins or a bonnet they had sewed. Louisa nodded and accepted the gifts which Henderson loaded into the carriage with her bags.

Louisa gathered up the palm full of coins she had been given and handed every one to Hannah, saying, "To help pay for my keep".

Louisa seemed to relax and enjoy the carriage ride, with Hannah distracting her at times with comments about the countryside they were travelling through. Richard Henderson had already prepared a room at the former schoolhouse, where he already had three other patients under his care.

The former school building had a more homely feel than the institutional former Mint building of St Peter's Hospital, which had always been designed to scare and overawe those who entered. It was also in the countryside rather than the centre of the city and, alighting from the carriage, Louisa showed little reluctance when walking into the asylum.

Her belongings were carefully placed where some staff could sort through them and Hannah and Richard Henderson led Louisa into the small bedroom. It was on seeing the bed that she started to become agitated for the first time. Hannah distracted her by showing her the trees through the large window, which overlooked a well-tended garden, but attempts to get her to sit on the bed were met with stubborn resistance.

Henderson had already thought ahead and he summoned the superintendent. She was Maayke, the same woman who had visited Louisa in the haystack a few years before, and spoken to Louisa in German. At that time she had been the wife of a Sea Captain. Now she was estranged from him and had stayed on in Bristol when he left on his ship. She had taken a job with Henderson as a superintendent caring for others. When he told her about the new patient she recounted to him how she had spoken with the girl and Henderson had decided that, as she spoke German and had a good experience with Louisa, she would be the ideal person to be her main carer.

She cheerily entered the room and spoke to Louisa in German but the reaction from Louisa was one of horror and she looked even more uncomfortable and distraught. Henderson had a second plan and he and Maayke went into action. They brought some fresh hay into the bedroom and removed the bed. Louisa lay down happily in the hay for her first night in the asylum.

Henderson gathered the other people who worked in the house together and he introduced them to Louisa; then he, Hannah More and Maayke gathered in the room for prayer.

Henderson spoke loudly. "O Glorious and Blessed God, Father, Son and Holy Spirit. Bless Louisa here and send your almighty love and care to her so that she may be healed. Help us your humble servants to support her and show her a life of comfort and peace. Amen."

At the end of the prayer everyone joined in the "Amen" with the loudest coming from Louisa herself, much to the amusement of Hannah and Maayke. They then left her for her first night of rest away from the haystack.

The next day Maayke helped Louisa get washed and dressed and, along with Richard Henderson, they went for a walk in the countryside nearby. Although she was civil and spoke a few short sentences in German in reply to questions, Louisa refused to have long conversations with Maayke and did not acknowledge that she had met her before while she was sitting in the haystack.

When they returned from the walk Henderson brought a pile of books into her bedroom and said they were there in case she wanted a distraction.

"No, reading is study," she said to him, "and study makes me mad."

During the whole of her time at Hendersons Louisa was never seen to look into a book. As the months went by she settled in well and enjoyed making little bracelets which she put on to her wrists and arms in vast numbers and was always keen to walk outside, whether the weather was good or bad. Her cough gradually improved and one day Maayke brought in a bed for her.

Once again she refused to sleep in it and eventually it was agreed that she should stay on a bed of straw.

The fine clothes that she had arrived at the haystack with had become rags and were thrown away. Basic replacement second-hand clothing was provided for her, thanks to the money from the Bathursts, William Turner and Hannah More, but Louisa often refused to wear it. As the weeks went on she would only get dressed to walk outside and most of the time would sit passively and calmly on the straw wrapped in a blanket. Henderson noted that she was "harmless and stupid" and "more inclined to idiocy than madness or lunacy."

Hannah More visited her frequently and often brought other people to see her. It was on one visit soon after her cough had receded that Hannah arrived with her sisters. On that day Louisa was in high spirits and was shaping her blankets into a robe that she wore about herself pretending to be royalty to everyone's amusement.

She had been at Hanham for several months when John Henderson, son of Richard, returned from London and was keen to meet with Louisa. He had been to view his own portrait at Joshua Reynolds' studio and, of course, had seen the other work by Palmer of the intriguing woman who lived in the haystack. He had also heard so much about her from his own father and his friend Hannah More.

He was around the same age as Louisa. Hannah and his father suggested that he might try to gently interrogate her and find out more about her. He first met her by joining her and his father for a walk around the local area. He pointed out some of the trees and found she knew a few of their names.

John Henderson was a skilled linguist, with knowledge of Spanish, Italian, German Persian, Arabic, Hebrew, Greek and Latin. His Latin and Greek scholarship enabled him to place fairly well any language spoken to him. Over a number of days he set about trying to work out where Louisa might have originated from. He concluded that she could understand both French and German but she only ever uttered the odd word in German and never spoke French to him.

As part of her confinement he, along with his father, decided to make medical notes on her - noting her looks, her behaviour and her attitude to things. This was to enable any changes - hopefully for the better - to be recognised. They had a plan that she could be nursed back into rejoining society one day, once her behaviour became more acceptable.

He reported in his notes that she had a pleasing and interesting countenance. She had fine expressive black eyes, and eyebrows; her complexion was wan, but not sickly; her under-jaw projected a little. Her hair was long and black, not thick but coming down on her forehead, her arms and hands were delicate and her fingers small and long.

His visits then took on more of an examination session than anything else and he passed on the findings to his father in the way of notes, setting out his questions to her, her answers and any clues they might give as to where she had started her life and how she had ended up in the haystack.

A typical encounter started with John Henderson saying how he was a friend and had come to see her. He reported she smiled and moved her bottom lip for some time without pronouncing a word. He then asked her to reach out her hand and she did so; with Henderson reporting that she reached out in the motions and attitude of a person of superior rank in life.

When questioned she rarely gave direct answers, if any at all, and often she gave exactly the same replies and phrases as she had done in a previous meeting.

One time he said to her, when they were planning a walk, "We are your friends; we have come to take you from this place. Will you go with us?"

Louisa replied, "Yes, but Mama must come and bring me clothes, and I must be dressed." She seemed to get quite emotional and pointed to her neck and shoulders and moved her fingers around to describe the shape of a fine dress.

Then she said, "We shall go in a coach with four horses, and we will make them gallop, and the people shall admire us as we pass," and with that she burst into fits of maniacal laughter and seemed to be imagining some kind of parade that she was enjoying.

She continued with her fantasy ride, "And we shall let all the glasses down - no that will be too cold." From this John Henderson concluded that she had good knowledge of a carriage and must have been accustomed to one in her upbringing - something not normally associated with rural people or the poor of the towns.

John Henderson pressed her. "But where shall we drive to?" Louisa replied, "home," and her clever inquisitor saw his chance:

"But where to? What home?"

Louisa replied, "O here and there, backwards and forwards, all around about." Louisa was waving her hand and seemed happy so he felt he could still push further, and said pointedly, "Louisa, shall we drive to Bohemia?"

She replied, "That is Papas own country." She was still laughing and seemed off her guard. John Henderson joined in the laughter and tried to push her on other questions, but got little information from her. Louisa, on all the occasions that Richard or John Henderson tried to get information out of her, was affable but gave little information about her past.

She spoke vaguely about Mama and Papa and on one occasion they felt they were getting somewhere as she was speaking fondly of Papa but when they questioned her about her Papa she explained she was talking about Richard Henderson.

At night the door to her room was locked and the caring team at Henderson's madhouse would listen at the door and could often hear her laughing. She seemed to be content living indoors providing she did not have to sleep in a bed and could reside in straw.

After a few months Amy and William Atkings took a ride out one day to see her at the behest of Hannah More, who felt that a visit from her old friends would be good for her. She greeted them warmly and knew who they were, tinkling the little bell at them, but was not particularly enthusiastic at their sudden appearance. It was almost as if she hadn't noticed they had not been around.

Amy sat with her and Louisa was playing with a Queen Anne half-crown that she had among her bits and pieces. She produced a black ribbon and asked Amy if she could help fix the coin to it. Amy used her sewing skills and made a black band with the coin on it that Louisa could wear on her arm. She kept kissing the coin and saying that it looked like her Mama. But there was less of the spark left in Louisa that Amy remembered from the early days in the haystack and after an hour or so Louisa seemed more interested in when the next delivery of food would be made to her room than she was in her visitors.

It was quite a long and inconvenient journey home on the cart with Jessie working hard to get them over the hills towards Flax Bourton. At one point a rain storm impeded their progress, turning the tracks across the countryside into a boggy mess and Amy was thoroughly wet and miserable sat up on the cart as William attempted to lead Jessie through. Jessie's old legs were slipping and sliding in the mud and then clattering on a stone, jolting the passengers.

When they returned to the cosiness of their cottage in Flax Bourton Amy vowed that they would not repeat the visit. The small portraits that Louisa had given them were hung on the wall near the stairs and remained the only reminder of the visitor that had once played such a major part in their lives. The people of Flax Bourton often talked about Louisa with fondness but the haystack was demolished and the harvests returned to normal.

As the days and months went by at Henderson's, Louisa became more institutionalised and resigned to her position. Her mysterious origins remained unresolved.

- *Chapter Five* -

The Pamphlet

RICHARD HENDERSON WAS certainly more caring of those in his charge than most other keepers of lunatics. He had a firm belief in God and a knowledge of the Bible that he passed on to others in an entertaining and engaging fashion. He still had a mild Irish accent from his early years at Ballygaran and that seemed to help him succeed when he was an itinerant preacher alongside John Wesley. The two were good friends and believed that God would find a way to bring the unfortunates back into useful life.

On the cold, frosty morning of January 15, 1782, Richard Henderson told Louisa that his good friend, the great preacher, John Wesley, was visiting the house that afternoon and would be coming in to see her. Louisa was wrapped in just a blanket and Richard and Maayke attempted to get her to put on some of the clothes they had provided for her. She stubbornly refused.

There was still a chill wind creeping through the cracks of the window frames at Henderson's madhouse when, fresh from his carriage, John Wesley arrived that afternoon. He wore a wig, powdered and curled, with the horse hair tumbling about his shoulders. He had a black frock coat and a collar with brilliant white material in two strips on his upper chest. His face was red from the carriage journey from Bristol as the January air had touched his skin, but he was a hardy traveller and within minutes of being greeted by his friend Richard Henderson he was asking about the various souls in his care.

Henderson took him on a tour of all the rooms. In each one, Wesley spoke to the inmate and took the large Bible from under his arm and, cradling it in his right elbow, opened pages to read passages or simply to provide a prop for his prayers.

When they got to Louisa the two men found her huddled on her hay with blankets around her. The tussle with Henderson earlier over getting dressed meant she retreated as she saw him. Henderson told Wesley he was likely to get more reaction from her if he left Wesley alone with her and the preacher nodded as Henderson left the room.

Having heard so much about this romantic creature who had lived in a haystack, from both Hannah More and Henderson, he was shocked and surprised to find such a pale and wan person. She was disconsolate and seemed full of sorrow and he could see the effect that being out in all winds and weathers had on her face and skin.

He reached out and she held his hand. After praying as he held her delicate hand, he asked her gently, "Hello Louisa, My name in John Wesley. Did Mr Henderson tell you about me?"

He noticed a peculiar sweetness in her eyes as she turned towards him, but she did not answer his question.

"You are Louisa aren't you?" asked Wesley.

"Yes, that is my name," she replied softly.

"Is there anything that you need?" he asked.

"No, Mr Henderson is good to me. I am well now." Louisa then started giggling and began to play with a few trinkets that were on the floor around her and Wesley noted that she was behaving like a child.

Louisa then started making a cape of the blanket and hiding her face behind it before sticking it out at Wesley and laughing like a child. He played along, shouting "boo" and she seemed to enjoy the game for 10 minutes or so before once again fiddling with her things and ignoring the visitor. After a few moments of being ignored Wesley decided there was little more for him to do on this visit. He said one last prayer for the lost soul in front of him and went to share a cup of tea with Henderson in his office.

"Richard, I do believe you have a rare talent for helping these patients I have seen. Hannah told me how ill Louisa was when she was brought here. She now seems quite recovered physically and let us hope that her mind will return from the child-like state she is in with God's grace.

"She clearly appreciates all you have done for her and appears to want for nothing. Has any more light been thrown on where she comes from or how she came to be in these strange circumstances?"

"Very little John. My son and our superintendent here, Maayke, have heard her speak a few words of German and she appears to understand French. She undoubtedly came to this country from overseas but how she got here and who she is, other than her Christian name of Louisa, is unknown. To be honest we are not even sure if this name was given to her by the good folk of Flax Bourton and she just adopted it, or whether it was always her name."

The two men fell into reminiscing about their earlier days preaching until Wesley took his leave as he was keen to get back to Bristol before darkness fell.

News that Wesley had visited Louisa excited some of Hannah More's other society friends and over the next few weeks there was a succession of visitors to see her. Most were society friends of Hannah from London and Bristol who she persuaded to visit Henderson's Asylum so that they could see the good work he was doing there for some of the less fortunate in society and so that they could donate to help to expand the support that could be given for those who had problems with their minds.

A visit to the small room where the Maid of the Haystack sat wrapped in a blanket on her bed of straw was always one of the highlights, with Hannah telling the tale of the portrait that had been painted of her and the mystery surrounding how she came to appear suddenly in Flax Bourton as if from nowhere.

Henderson had started to categorise some of the types of malady that he cared for. Some had been suffering from birth from an affliction that they were born with; some developed deranged symptoms as a result of Opium or drink; others had suffered a blow to the head or an accident or had gone through some kind of traumatic experience that had changed their behaviour. He was convinced that Louisa had either had a physical accident or had suffered an emotional trauma.

As time went by Louisa's condition seemed to worsen. She rarely wanted to get dressed anymore, or go out on walks; she preferred to just sit in her room staring blankly or fiddling with coins and small objects, including the little bell, that she always kept about her. They seemed to be her only comfort. The activities and games that were part of Henderson's programme of rehabilitation were ignored to such an extent that eventually they left Louisa alone and no longer offered them to her.

On one of Hannah More's visits to bring money to Henderson they discussed the future of Louisa and it was decided to take one more chance on finding out if anyone had any information about her.

Hannah More suggested they publish her story in the local newspaper with an appeal for anyone to come forward who might be related or have some information about her. The enthusiasm from the Bathursts for supporting Louisa was waning and it was felt that perhaps wider publicity would find Louisa's family.

Henderson said, "We must put in some of the things that have happened since she has been here. How she burst into tears when hearing German but has answered a few questions in that language. Maayke also reported that a few weeks ago a coach pulled by four horses passed along the Upper Bath Road here and Louisa ran to the window with Maayke to watch it go by.

"She excitedly exclaimed: 'A wonderful sight. Truly. My father's coach was drawn by eight horses.' We have no idea whether that was a little insight into her past life as nobility or whether it is simply her wild imagination. We try to capture any clue that we are given."

Hannah arranged for the article to appear and over the next few weeks there were visits from people anxious to see her.

Saddest of these were from four different couples who had

lost children years before who would now be about Louisa's age. Each of the couples arrived expectantly, hoping that at last they might be reunited with their lost daughter, and each left forlorn after finding nothing in Louisa that reminded them of their child and no recognition or acknowledgement from her.

Many people who spoke different languages came to speak to Louisa to see if she would converse with them but the more people who came in speaking in strange tongues and accents then the less she was inclined to react.

A rumour circulated that she was the Queen of Denmark; another that she was the wife of a rich merchant in Bath who had fled from his violent behaviour. Another story circulated that she was the daughter of a German Baron. Henderson took up this by writing a letter to the Baron in question, but got a reply that there was nothing in the description that made him believe she was his daughter.

Over two years Louisa's condition deteriorated little by little. Wesley noticed as much when he visited again on March 6th 1784. Two years after his first visit he found he could only spend a few minutes in her company because of her behaviour.

In his notes of that day he called her the "lost Louisa" and described how "she is now in a far more deplorable case than ever. She used to be mild, though silly; but now she is quite furious. I doubt the poor machine cannot be repaired in this life".

Hope of bringing Louisa back into polite society was now lost and with it some of the funding of those who were helping to pay for her upkeep. Hannah More and her sisters, along with the Bathursts, were now pretty much the only ones sufficiently interested to keep funds flowing. Hannah was still determined to get to the bottom of where Louisa came from.

Then the madhouse had a new resident - John Henderson - son of the owner. The man who, just a few years before, had been trying to get to the bottom of Louisa's madness with his clever questioning was now sleeping in a bed in a locked room down the corridor. He had been behaving more and more eccentrically in London. At first it had been drinking, smoking and opium but for a while now he had concentrated his efforts on various ways of contacting the dead. He firmly believed he could make a breakthrough to communicate with those who had passed beyond and had started dedicating every waking second to this venture.

It became such an obsession that his friends began to shun him. He started going to bed at daybreak and not getting up until the afternoon so that he could spend time in the dead of night attempting his communications. He started starving himself for days on end then stripping to the waist and dousing himself in water and putting a shirt on his soaking wet body in order to free his mind.

Hannah More was distraught at the way the lad, who had been such a brilliant scholar, was now in such a sad state. When friends in London finally brought him home to his father because of his odd behaviour Hannah was also concerned that Louisa might see him in this condition. How would she cope with seeing someone who had previously been a pillar of the establishment, and her inquisitor, behaving so oddly?

Richard Henderson, too, was devastated by the peculiar behaviour of his clever son. Here he was, a doctor lauded by many as the best person for treating those with madness in the country and yet, seemingly, he could do little about his own son's obsession with the afterlife and his use of alcohol and drugs. He began to lose heart in his project as his son's behaviour became more and more pronounced and more well known. He confessed to Hannah More that he was considering closing Henderson's madhouse so that he could concentrate on his own family.

Hannah discussed with her sisters what they should do if Henderson should decide to close the asylum. They considered whether they might take over the madhouse but did not feel qualified or able to take it on.

It was still playing on her mind when she next called in at Belmont to see William Turner in the summer of 1784. She had arranged to call at the house on her way into Bristol from her home in Wrington. Hannah, William and Joe sat outside the house with its magnificent view across the valley to the sea, with drinks served to them by the domestic help.

Joe was showing off a new beaver fur hat that he had bought. It was the latest fashion brought across from the exotic adventures in America. Although it was a warm day he sat outside with it on his head, much to Hannah's amusement.

"It really suits you Joe but I think really it will be better later in the year," said Hannah, laughing.

"I know, but I love it so much. It is going to come into its own and be really warm when we get the winter snows here. Apparently there are all kinds of beasts being discovered in Western America at the moment. I have heard that unicorns and dragons could yet be discovered."

"Oh that would be fantastic," said William. "There must be some truth in the stories of unicorns and dragons. I think basically man just killed them off here. But in those wild lands they are probably still roaming free. It is so exciting. I've heard there is a whole mountain made of crystals that has been discovered."

"Yes," said Hannah. "But if we are to exploit the lands and bring back these wonderful things we need to do it with some care. The system of slavery is just not right and that has grown with just about every merchant in Bristol involved in trading people. Even some of the most pious people in the Methodist Church, who are against slavery, own plantations and get their own wealth from it. There is a movement Joe and many of us are campaigning for change."

Turner remarked, "Of course you are right Hannah, but there are also a lot of problems closer to home that we need to address first. It is great that you have returned to Bristol and you are tackling so many things. There is so much to do in this area for both your literary and philanthropic work without having to worry about America or be in London the whole time."

Sipping her drink, Hannah replied, "My main focus at the moment is in setting up rural Sunday Schools. I am writing some tracts and plays that highlight the plight of the rural community. It is incredible how much simply teaching some of the farm labourers to read can make a difference. There is a huge desire for learning and, despite what some of our betters claim, many of the peasantry have hearts of gold and will do anything for each other.

"Often it is those from the lowliest backgrounds who make the most of their talents while those born with privilege and a good background simply waste it. Look at John Henderson. He was a brilliant scholar and I was one of the people who helped him go to Oxford to study and yet now he is behaving abominably and embarrassing his father with talk of communicating with the dead and his drunken antics."

"William, you must meet the milkmaid I am sponsoring. That's another "project" as you call it. She is desperately poor and has six children Richard Vaughan found her living in a stable and yet she has written the most fantastic poetry. I am putting together money from various sponsors to help her. Once they read examples of her poetry they all want to support it.

"Her name is Anne Yearsley. The idea is that we can edit and publish her work and make a good return on the money put in and enable her to live a better life. She was writing the poems late at night while her children were asleep. I have organised a maid to look after her children so she can find more time to write.

"We have Bishops, Lords and ladies on our list of those likely to want a part of this project. They will see a return on their money; Anne will live a life as a writer instead of a milkmaid and the amounts we make can go into other good works."

Turner warmed to the project and Hannah told them how Anne Yearsley was calling her "Stella" in some of the poems in reference to her being a "star" for helping her. Joe suggested that, in return, the poems be published under the pen-name Lactilla as a reference to Anne Yearsley's background as a milkmaid, which amused Hannah greatly.

"I was talking to Anne the other day and telling her about the mystery of Louisa, and how she so loved the poetry when you read it to her here. We are trying desperately to get more information about her."

Joe looked at William. The two of them seemed nervous at the conversation turning to Louisa.

"What's wrong?" asked Hannah. "So many people came forward as a result of the newspaper appeal, but nothing has come of it."

William Turner felt that this was the time to tell Hannah about the secret manuscript they had found.

"Joe and I discovered something within the Masonic Hall some time ago that we believe might relate to Louisa. There are many parallels with her story. It is a long document but we will get it for you to read and copy. But please, don't let anyone know where you got the information as it is against the Masonic Code for us to pass this on to you. We know, however, that you will do the right thing."

"I am intrigued," said Hannah and immediately started asking questions, all of which the two men diverted, saying that she must read the document and draw her own conclusions as to whether it has any significance to Louisa.

A few weeks later the men had borrowed the document once again while at a Lodge meeting and had it delivered to Hannah's home in Wrington with instructions for her to copy it and return it.

Hannah's first reaction on reading the document was astonishment. The detail it contained gave her no doubt that this illegitimate daughter of the Emperor existed. To see the name of Thomas Dunckerley, so well known as one of the powerful men who had major influence in Bristol and beyond, embroiled in the scandal showed that it was quite possible that Felicia, mentioned in the story, could have been brought to Bristol.

The similarity between the pet name, Licia, and the name Louisa, when spoken with a foreign accent, was not lost on her. But there was a six year gap between the events of the document and the appearance of Louisa in the haystack and there was no explanation of what might have happened during that time. If she had been put into the care of the Freemasons how had the girl come to be unaccompanied and why had they not taken her back into their care?

In copying the document Hannah studied the twists and turns of the story again and again and one aspect that fascinated her was the carriage accident. She went to Henderson with a medical doctor with the intention of examining Louisa to see if there was any evidence of such an accident.

The doctor reported that Louisa had a very large scar on the lower part of her head behind her ear. This could well have been from an accident and could have affected her brain. He also reported a wound near her breast, which appeared to be from violence or an accident of some sort.

Hannah now believed that this physical evidence showed even more clearly that Louisa may be the lost Felicia, illegitimate sister of the Queen of France, Marie Antoinnette, who at this moment was just about the most famous and powerful woman in the world. But there was another check she wanted to make. She needed to reveal the story in confidence to her closest friend, Eva Marie Garrick; after all she had been a dancer as a youth in Germany and had known the Emperor and Empress.

The meeting took place in London. Hannah could not trust the copy of the document to be sent so carried it personally. She sat for a full half hour in silence while Eva Marie read it through.

Finally Eva Marie turned to her. "I believe it," she said. "In truth I had a relationship with the Emperor. He was a charming and powerful man, but also very caring. I was the young dancer Violette, I had just turned 20. I was friendly with both the Emperor and the Empress but my relationship with the Emperor got out of hand.

"The Empress was really all-powerful; her husband, weak. She insisted that I was banished to England. When I arrived here I could not speak a word of English. It was only thanks to my talent as a dancer and the theatre that I survived. Through the theatre I met Davie and we were married within three years of my arrival here.

"Everything about this story rings true. It was well-known that the Princess of Auersperg, who was 30 years younger than him, was his lover. If they had a child then the story about a nunnery sounds like exactly the sort of thing they would do. It is the Catholic way."

"Now I think back to when I saw her at the haystack there was some similarity in features to the Emperor, but nobody could possibly be sure. Are you convinced Louisa is this person though?"

Hannah replied, "No, I can't be absolutely sure. There is nothing among her possessions now that link her to those days. Her fine dresses have gone. People say that in the past she showed them portraits like those mentioned in the papers, but they are not at Henderson's. She is too far gone now in her madness to tell us anything sensible. There are only glimpses of sanity about her from time to time.

"The situation has been made worse by John Henderson's confinement. He discovered some things about her but now we must question his own accounts of things. But I know that if I was Marie Antoinette and I knew I had a sister who was in trouble I would want to help her. There are no people closer in the world to me than my sisters and sisterly love runs deep. We have to somehow get this story to Marie Antoinette so that she can step in. We only have limited funds to help Louisa. Imagine if we could reach out to the Queen of France in this way and bring some of her wealth to help the poor here."

The two women discussed how they might influence Marie Antoinette. Both knew the power of pamphlets and printed material. Hannah was now being published regularly with her religious tracts and poetry. She was also working on the Lactilla publication of Anne Yearsley's work.

Mrs Garrick had been involved in all manner of publications of her husband's plays and among their friends were writers, printers and artists. Eva Marie had contacts across Europe and they decided to put together a pamphlet in French that would be released in France telling the story of Felicia and linking it to Louisa. All mention of the Freemasons would be taken out of it but it would be as close to the truth as the two could publish.

The next few days saw the women working on little else but the document. Once all mention of the Masonic link was taken out of the document they could bring one or two of their male friends into the picture.

The new version of the story of Felicia had to look as if it had been written by someone in Europe and Eva Marie's background helped. She ensured all the European aristocrats involved in the story were mentioned. Within days it had been translated into French, sent to a printer that Eva Marie knew in Austria and arrangements were made to ensure that it found its way to the French Royal Family.

Under the title "The Stranger, A True History," the pamphlet set out the story of Louisa's plight in the haystack in Bristol, outlined her recent move to the madhouse in Hanham, using the material that had already been circulated in newspapers. The women then added in the detail and elements of the document that had been recovered from the safe.

No author was named, to disguise the fact that it came from Hannah and Eva Marie, and the printers left off their usual mark. There was a huge appetite for reading matter among the rich in

Europe and the pamphlet was placed in the hands of Swedish nobleman Axel von Fersne, a close friend of Marie Antoinette. He was attending card parties at a small cottage in the grounds of Versailles and had the eye of the Queen. Having recently returned from fighting in America, he cut quite an intriguing figure and rumours were circulating in court that he and Marie Antoinette had a very close relationship indeed and that he was the Queen's lover.

Hannah and Eva Marie were delighted with their work and over the weeks and months following the publication a number of letters and visitors arrived at Henderson's madhouse once again, either hoping that they could identify Louisa or purporting to know something about her background.

The most intriguing was a man who arrived in a travelling carriage. It was attended by servants and he went to see Henderson demanding to see the Maid of the Haystack.

While he was inside the house his servants told others who worked in the madhouse that they had come from abroad and had travelled for a day and a night just to get to see the Maid of the Haystack. It turned into a very fleeting visit, but Henderson was amazed at the man's reaction when he took him to Louisa's room.

He simply said, "It is her!" then ran back outside and got back into his carriage and ordered those around him to drive off.

Henderson thought it was most peculiar and noted that Louisa would not look up until after the man left. Although Henderson quizzed her she appeared to know nothing of who the man might be.

Henderson reported the incident to Hannah More and Eva Marie and they speculated on whether this was, at last, some kind of visit prompted by the French Royal Family but they could not be sure.

Hannah and Eva Marie discussed other ways they might bring Louisa's plight to the notice of important people in society.

Every day Hannah was also selecting the poems that were sent to her by Anne Yearsley, editing them and arranging for the way they might be published.

She was herself a best-selling author and was spending time with Thomas Cadell, London-based bookseller and publisher and son of a Bristol bookseller, arranging the poems into a form that they both knew would sell well. She had talked to Thomas about the plight of Louisa and how she was hoping to shed some light on her background by publicising the story.

It was Cadell who suggested that a poem by Anne Yearsley about the Maid of the Haystack in her publication might help. After all a romantic poem about a forlorn woman in a haystack couldn't fail to excite interest.

Hannah More arranged for Anne to be taken to Flax Bourton to see where the haystack had been and wrote to Henderson to arrange a visit. She told him, "Anne has a great way of capturing the ways of working and rural people. I'm sure she can write a poem about what it was like for Louisa in the haystack. If you can arrange for a visit so that she can perhaps get acquainted with Louisa that will help her with her descriptions of her time in the haystack."

So it was that, in January 1785, Richard Henderson let Anne Yearsley into his madhouse. She brought with her some milk and some cheese and was shown into the little room where Louisa sat on a bundle of hay. There was a dreary light coming into the room.

"Hello, I'm Anne. I've brought some milk for you," she said.

Louisa was pleased to have a visitor, especially one bearing her favourite drink. There was also something down-to-earth and comforting about this woman, unlike the usual excited society people who visited. Anne reminded her of the ordinary women who she had spent time with at Flax Bourton; someone without the airs and graces of the More sisters, who were her most frequent visitors.

"Hannah told me about you," said Anne and immediately sensed a less friendly response from Louisa. She changed tack and unwrapped some cheese. Louisa came over to sit by her and they sat in silence drinking the milk and breaking off pieces of cheese to eat.

Anne decided to talk about herself. "I'm a milkmaid. I'm also another of Hannah's projects. She likes my poetry and she has helped me in many ways, but I do feel a little trapped by her. She has started to tell me what I should or should not write; what would work for her society friends. I'm a bit fed up of being paraded at her posh dinner parties. How do you get on with her?"

Louisa turned sad eyes to Anne. "It is hard for me to remember things," she said quietly.

"Do you remember being in the haystack?"

"Yes, of course. I loved it there. The people were very kind. We had milk!" She held up her little cup and smiled and Anne chuckled too, replying, "Well, you can't get better than that."

Louisa continued: "I don't know what I am doing here. There is nothing but misery here. Inside a house. I am just waiting to die."

Anne reached out and held her hand. Louisa looked overwhelmed and exhausted and grateful for a friend. They sat holding on to each other for some time.

"What was it like in the haystack?"

"It was cold and miserable in the winter. The wind and rain could be bad. But the people were so nice. I saw so many people and in the summer it was a wonderful place to be with the flowers and the trees and the sunshine."

Suddenly Louisa was animated once again and smiling and laughing and she seemed to go off to another world in her mind. She started dancing around the room, alarmingly. And singing. Singing loudly.

"But though you've suffered for my sake, contented will we be
For I love my love because I know my love loves me."

Anne knew the song and clapped along and laughed as Louisa leapt around the room, her mind far away on the distant memory.

The noise brought Richard Henderson into the room, closely followed by his son, John, who appeared drunk and leered at Anne.

"I think you are getting her a little too excited. Maybe time to call it a day," said Richard.

Anne felt sorry for Louisa, who on the appearance of the two men retreated back to her pile of hay. It reminded her of her own cows retreating after they had been milked. Richard Henderson steered his son out of the room and Anne spent a few more moments with Louisa, who was now looking away from her and no longer engaging.

Anne left the remainder of the cheese and a small jug of milk next to Louisa and took her leave. Calling into the office to thank Richard Henderson before walking out of the madhouse, words were already forming in her mind for a poem.

The next day the servant that Hannah More supplied to Anne was looking after her children so she took up her pen and wrote a poem, which she called Clifton Hill. The weather outside was dreadful, wet and cold and she imagined the journey from her workplace there in Clifton across the fields to Flax Bourton and the place where Louisa had lived for those years in the haystack.

Her mood, and the growing resentment she was feeling for the way that Hannah More felt she owned her, came out in the poetry. She felt an affinity with Louisa. Maybe both of them were just being toyed with by this rich lady. How much simpler life was just living in the countryside.

She expressed how Louisa must feel plucked from her pleasurable living space to now be incarcerated in that miserable room in Hanham while Hannah More and her sisters enjoyed their parties and showed her off to their friends. In a way there was a real parallel between herself and the poor lunatic.

In truth Louisa was not coping well with the surroundings at Henderson's madhouse. His early enthusiasm for treating those in his care with greater dignity than other institutions had been sorely tested by the state of his own son. The Maid of The Haystack showed no signs of being able to recover to live a normal life as he hoped; his son's descent into madness seemed similarly impossible to halt and others in his care showed violence and behaviour that he found harder and harder to cope with.

His theory that prayers and good treatment would help to bring these people back to normality was being challenged every day. He was not sure how much longer he could keep the madhouse open and began to consider whether it would be best if he passed his inmates on to St Peter's Hospital.

Back in London Anne Yearsley's poem was published and rekindled interest once again in the 'romantic lunatic', the Maid of the Haystack. Hannah More was not pleased with the tone of the poem and her relationship with the milkmaid was becoming more strained every day.

Now, many of the benefactors who had initially helped to pay for Louisa had fallen by the wayside with other projects and, with Henderson threatening to close the madhouse any day, Hannah felt there was even more pressure to get a breakthrough in finding out whether Louisa was indeed the offspring of European royalty. She was used to projects running their course as people dropped them. Enthusiasm for schools and other projects she ran often waned after a little while among the wealthy, or they found themselves with a little less disposable money. Despite the best efforts of Hannah and her sisters it was always as if they were trying to fill a bucket with a hole in it. Besides which, the sisters were always coming up with new projects and often found that by moving people on to new projects they ended others.

The Bathursts, however, had continued to support Louisa and regularly talked to Hannah about her welfare and what might be the best future for her. The women decided that maybe an English translation of the French document might help to bring some interest in. Of course they needed to keep it separate from Hannah's usual publications as they were keen for it to appear that it was not from them.

A London publisher and printer called Henry Lasher Gardner had been an apprentice with the Bathursts and had now taken over his father's print works in The Strand. He was enlisted to produce a new version of the pamphlet entitled "A Narrative of Facts supposed to throw light on the history of the Bristol Stranger known by the name of The Maid of the Haystack". To throw people off the scent the women insisted that it should say "translated from the French" on the front. Lady Bathurst paid for it to be produced.

Other printers were arranged in Bath, Bristol, Gloucester and Cheltenham, where there was still a lot of interest in Louisa's story. They ran off copies of the pamphlet that Henry Lasher Gardner produced. Sales of the pamphlet went well and helped to replace the funds that had depleted for Louisa's upkeep.

- Chapter Six -

The Austrian Ambassador to France

HANNAH MORE AND Eva Marie waited with some anticipation at the Adelphi in London. They had received a note from Horace Walpole, the Fourth Earl of Oxford, which said he would like to come to see them. As a Whig politician, and son of the late Sir Robert Walpole, who had effectively run the country for 20 years, he was well-known to both of them.

They had met Horace at many London events and had both read his novel of some years before - The Castle of Otranto - which had been something of a sensation as it merged romance and horror. Most exciting about the note they had received was that he was planning to bring with him European nobleman Florimont-Claude Mercy-Argenteau.

Florimont-Claude was known to be very close to the French royal family, having played a major part in making the royal marriage happen when he was Austrian Ambassador and had played an influential part in the Courts of both King Louis XV and XVI.

The two men duly arrived mid afternoon in a carriage that Walpole had ridden in from his home at Strawberry Hill, London, picking up the Ambassador on the way.

Both men were thin and quite gaunt. The Ambassador carried his hat in his hands and seemed a little nervous and almost scared of the two women as he was welcomed into the room dominated by the painting of Garrick over the fireplace.

To make conversation both men admired the painting and Walpole told the Count all about the wonderful theatrical work of Garrick and the many plays and entertainments that he himself had attended, praising the work of Garrick and his sadness at the man's demise.

A servant brought in some tea and eventually the four of

them sat down around a table and it became obvious that now was the time to talk business.

Horace Walpole produced a copy of the English pamphlet from a small bag he had with him and at the same time the Ambassador, Comte de Mercy-Argentau, reached into his bag and produced the French language version.

Walpole looked at the two women. "We have come about these two documents. Or to be more precise we have come to talk about Louisa and see how we can help. I have known about her for some time and I have been in correspondence with William Turner at Belmont, through some mutual associations we have.

" My friend Florimont-Claude has come from Paris. He has been investigating the story on behalf of none-other than Marie Antoinette, the Queen of France, following these publications, and he has some interesting news for you."

The women looked surprised to see the two very powerful men holding the documents that they had sent out into the world, but both looked at the Ambassador to see what he had to say.

He spoke softly in a French accent, saying, "Madam More, I am aware that you are paying the upkeep of this person in Bristol and that there has been some speculation about the possibility that she may be the daughter of the Emperor and therefore a half-sister of Marie Antoinette.

"The Queen asked me to investigate and I have been gathering information in Bordeaux, about the woman who lived there and in my native Belgium. A few weeks ago, a nobleman who had known the woman in Bordeaux travelled to Bristol at my behest and went to see the unfortunate Louisa in her place at the madhouse. He confirms it is indeed the same woman."

The two women gasped at this confirmation, but before they could say any more Walpole interjected with some more information.

He said, "I am very much aware of Louisa and a few years ago I was very concerned to hear she was confined by necessity to a cell. I thought at that time it was lack of finance that meant she was having to be held this way and offered to make a contribution. I understand, in fact, that the deplorable state of her mind occasioned her confinement in a cell for lunatics.

"My knowledge of her comes from my Masonic Brethren, and it is clear that much of the information in these two pamphlets has come from sources there. The Brethren I have spoken to were never convinced that the woman in the haystack could be the esteemed daughter of the Emperor, and felt much more sure that she was another missing person from Hamburgh who had on occasion been confused with her. But this information from my friend Florimont-Claude here changes much."

Hannah More and Eva Marie looked at each other and smiled, but there was some resignation in her voice when Hannah spoke.

"This is great news, but you are right that Louisa seems to have deteriorated in her mind. There is also the problem that my friend Henderson may not be able to keep the madhouse going for much longer. His own son is there and that has sadly taken its toll on him. Everyone has worked so hard to improve conditions for those suffering in this way but very soon there will need to be another intervention to find a new home for Louisa."

Florimont-Claude looked at Walpole and leaned forward. "I believe I may be able to help there. The Queen is obviously keen to help and also avoid any scandal. There are many lies and rumours about her already and this pamphlet has not helped, with some people upset that she should live in such comfort in the Palace of Versailles while an illegitimate sister of the same age lies on straw in a cell in a madhouse.

"I discussed the matter with her a few weeks ago and I am here today to offer to take Louisa to a new home being created in a hamlet that is being built in the park of the Chateau de Versailles. I have spoken to members of the Brethren here in England about the conditions that Louisa enjoyed when she lived in the haystack. I understand she is happiest if in a haystack outside and hates being confined inside."

Hannah More nodded. "That is true. Her happiest days were truly when she was in touch with the countryside and she has always seemed to have some kind of fear of being confined between walls. But there is little we can do. She needs to be confined for her own safety. But tell me more about this new facility that is being built. Is it for those who are suffering from madness?"

"Not exactly Madam," said the French nobleman. "It is called L'hameau de la Reine" - in English that is the Queen's Hamlet. The architect Richard Mique drew up the plans and it is right beside the Royal Palace and the Queen herself will live there much of the year.

"In many ways it is based on the typical English village with a duck pond, some farmhouses, orchards and flower gardens. There will be working farms which will provide eggs, milk, lamb and beef for the Royal household. The Queen will be able to relax there, wearing the clothes of country folk and mixing with the country people who will move in there.

"Some of the lakes and canals and winding paths are already in place. I spoke a few weeks ago to the Queen and the head farmer, Monsieur Vally Bussard. Work is well underway to create the farms and buildings. The idea is to have a covered barn with a haystack inside that could be home to Louisa. She could walk safely in the grounds as it is kept secure to protect the Queen. She could attend some of the fine events and maybe recover and become part of the social scene. We know she spoke French well while in Bordeaux so she will quickly re-learn and live out her life in what to all appearances is a perfect rural village."

Eva Marie giggled at the prospect. "It sounds incredible. Maybe I could come and live there myself. Imagine such a beautiful place!"

The two men smiled and laughed at the widow's suggestion

and enthusiasm. Hannah More stepped in. "This is such fantastic news. For a long time we have wondered if anyone would ever solve the mystery of Louisa. The stories seem fanciful in some ways but they also ring true whenever you speak to others. She has never made any claims herself, but it seems so likely that she is the daughter - and she does bear a resemblance to the Emperor without a doubt."

The conversation went on for two hours. It seemed that the haystack home within the grounds of Versailles would be ready for Louisa in around a year's time. Hannah More said that she was not sure that Henderson would keep his madhouse open that long and maybe the best course of action would be to move Louisa to an asylum in London until the French Royal Family was able to take her into her new home in France.

Walpole said, "Obviously all of this must be kept strictly secret. I am sure that I can find members among the Brotherhood who can help with the transfer to France, but yes that will be easier from London if you can move her here as a temporary measure. It will be good for her to be assessed at a good hospital in London so that a report can be drawn up that outlines Louisa's health and state of mind. This report can go with her to those who will be caring for her in France."

"Yes," said Hannah, "I will make the arrangements. In many ways she will be going home - and back to a haystack environment. That would be perfect. She always enjoyed the attention of visitors when she was at Flax Bourton so will not be bothered by visitors to the Royal Palace. I believe she might enjoy being given some attention once again and meeting different people."

Florimont-Claude said, "I believe Louisa could become an attraction in herself at the "Jardin Anglais". The romantic story about her is now well-known in France among the educated classes."

The two men took their leave. Hannah immediately got

her writing set out and started carefully composing a letter to Henderson. She also wrote to Guy's Hospital in London, which was fast gaining a good reputation for the care of the insane. She told them that she wished to transfer a lunatic woman from Bristol and enquired after fees and arrangements that would have to be made.

It seemed the mystery of the Maid of The Haystack had been solved at last and she was to be reunited in France with the sister she had never known.

- Chapter Seven -

Guy's Hospital

HENDERSON KNEW THAT the days of the madhouse were numbered. His son's increasingly distressing condition had taken its toll on him - and it seemed that despite his best efforts Louisa's condition had simply worsened.

For several months Louisa had increasingly become placid and introverted and had done little but lie on her straw all day. Her complexion was now pale and, although only in her thirties, her skin showed signs of ageing and weathering from the years of living outside in the haystack. She would pass for an elderly woman and she had little or no energy most days.

So when Hannah More's letter arrived, transferring Louisa to another hospital was an obvious next step that in many ways was a relief. In recent years Hannah had agreed with Henderson that her contribution towards Louisa's upkeep should be reduced from £50 a year to £30, and that also was a factor.

Some weeks later Hannah More arrived at Henderson's and told him she had secured a place in Guy's Hospital for just £10 a year. Henderson had taken the decision to close his hospital and convert the building to a school and with both now convinced that, sadly, Louisa was unlikely to improve in her current circumstances in the way that they had hoped, it was an easy and businesslike meeting between them.

What Hannah had not told Henderson was the longer term plan of Louisa moving to France and the fact she had told Guy's Hospital it would be a temporary move.

Hannah went along the corridor and found Louisa simply lying in some hay. She sat up when Hannah came in, took the ribbons out of Hannah's cap and made them into little bracelets and that seemed to give her a simple pleasure. Hannah then tied the ribbons into Louisa's hair, which was still fine and dark. But when she held up a small mirror she carried with her in her bag she seemed shocked at her own reflection, tore at the ribbons and wrapped herself up in a blanket on the bed in distress.

Hannah told her that the hospital run by Mr Henderson was soon to close and that she was to move to another one in London. There was no reaction, except one of resigned acceptance from Louisa.

She whispered conspiratorially to Louisa, "We are trying to arrange for you to move to France where you can live in a little village with its own haystack, close to the Royal Family there. Lots of the finest people in Europe will be there."

There was a glimmer of reaction from Louisa and she said slowly, but distractedly, "France... I lived in France. Went to the finest parties..." her voice trailed off. There was no enthusiasm and Hannah wasn't certain if the poor soul hadn't forgotten what was said almost as soon as she said it. They fell into silence and a few minutes later Richard Henderson came in and together they said a prayer and left.

A few weeks later it was Richard Henderson and Maayke who accompanied Louisa in the carriage to London. It was June 1786 and although mail coaches were making the journey regularly in around 15 hours they were to take two days over the journey.

They stopped in a boarding house in Marlborough overnight with Maayke sleeping in the same room as Louisa to look after her. It was there that, for the first time in many, many years, Louisa slept in a bed. The softness of the sheets felt good to her and Maayke was surprised that there was none of the expected fuss at being in a conventional room. Maybe it was the rigours of the journey that had tired her out. For whatever reason Louisa settled down well to sleep and there were no problems in the night with her.

The next day they continued their journey to London and it was a weary group that arrived in the early evening to be greeted at Guy's Hospital by an efficient matron with a London accent called Maud Strong. She very firmly and with no nonsense put the exhausted Louisa into a bedroom and settled her down with a drink before giving her belongings to an assistant, who started processing them and talking to Louisa, who said not a word.

"Is she mute?" Maud asked Maayke and Henderson.

"She has been speaking less and less but in the early days she spoke more. Although, to be honest it is very repetitive. She also seems to understand German and French."

Maud eyed up Louisa, who was now lying on the bed. Louisa was put in a room with three beds. The other two were occupied by old women, slowly dying. An assistant helped Louisa with her clothes. She was so tired that she made little fuss as she was tucked into only the second bed she had slept in for many years. Maud, Maayke and Henderson left her there being watched over by a nurse assistant and continued their conversation in a small office at the end of the corridor out of her earshot.

Henderson handed over a sheaf of papers. "Here are all the details we have about her. It includes our observations of her and everything that we know."

Maud studied the papers for a while and looked at her own notes. "I see that the fees of £10 a year are being paid by Miss Hannah More and that she has agreed to continue those payments for as long as the patient is here. That all seems to be in order."

Maud shuffled through the paperwork and came to the pamphlet giving the account of the Maid of the Haystack.

Maayke saw her reading it and spoke up. "Yes, you may have an issue when she is not so tired. In our hospital she always slept on a bed of straw to replicate the haystack. Last night and just now are the first times we have successfully settled her in a bed. To be honest we didn't really persist much back at the beginning. She used to get so distressed it was easier to let her sleep on the floor."

Maud smiled. "I'm sure we can cope. We have people here

who refuse to wear clothes; many who sleep on the floor in their own filth. She seems very passive at the moment but we know how the moon affects lunatics and we can cope with them.

"Ah yes. The Maid of the Haystack. In the old days she would have been a star attraction for our open days and it would save people like Miss More having to pay out so much. I used to work at Bedlam and we would have thousands of people through on a Bank Holiday to look and learn from the inmates.

"A good looking woman who slept on a bed of straw with this story behind her would have had them queueing down the street. I think we had a lad with a hairy face who was Lion Boy; one who didn't stop blaspheming and swearing who was the Devil's Disciple."

"Yes," said Henderson, warming to the theme. "I visited many madhouses, including Bedlam on some of those open events. I remember the Welshman Mad for Cheese, the mad politician, the war-mongering general, the Emperor and, of course, the fair Ophelia, who was lovesick.

"When I first came to London we visited Bedlam, the Tower of London, Fisher's Folly and Westminster Abbey in the space of a few days. All the tourist spots. By far the most exciting and entertaining was seeing the characters in Bedlam."

Maud retorted, "Yes, I looked after some of them characters. There were great life lessons for many of the people who visited. Often people would bring their children along to show them what might happen to them if they did not behave in a Godly way. Most importantly though were the coins we would get in the bucket. It kept the hospital going and helped us to look after the poor souls and keep them off the streets bothering people.

"Since we restricted visitors we have more lunatics killing themselves. I'm sure it is because they also used to get a lot out of seeing the visitors. Sitting all day staring into space in your own company is not good for anyone. If I had my way we would bring it back in some way. It worked well.

"Without a doubt the Maid of the Haystack would be a great draw. After all, it seems she basically financed herself by being on show before you took her into your care."

"Yes, that's correct," said Henderson.

"My house in Bristol was set up to be very different to Bedlam and all the other hospitals. As a Methodist I was not welcomed at Bedlam after a while - they actually said that preachers were encouraging madness! We took a different view, more like the one you have here today. More about caring. But I'm afraid I can't cope now.

"My own son has succumbed to madness and I am just going to care for him and continue my preaching. We are slowly but surely emptying the house of lunatics. I have another one going to St Peter's Hospital when I get back to Bristol.

"Strangely, as I get older I become less sure of what is the right thing to do with these unfortunates. There is merit in many methods."

Henderson and Maayke said their goodbyes and went to a boarding house that had been arranged for them by Hannah More. The next morning they started the carriage journey back towards the South West.

A few days later they were able to meet with Hannah and her sister Patty in Bristol to inform them that Louisa was quite comfortable in her new temporary abode in London. There were no issues and she was now settled in a bed.

In truth Hannah More was already more engrossed in her next project than in the welfare of Louisa. She had arranged the regular payments and was just waiting for clarity from France on how Louisa might be moved to the Jardin Anglais in Versailles so she could see out the rest of her days. Being moved to somewhere further South, she reasoned, would be beneficial as the weather would be warmer than in Somerset. There was a plan for her to have her own haystack, which would be quite luxurious and which would mean other people around for Louisa to interact with. It had been an undeniable fact that Louisa was happiest living outdoors.

She reasoned that once among her own kind again Louisa might recover sufficiently to live a relatively normal and successful life. She was far from the lost cause that many of the lunatics that Hannah had witnessed were.

Hannah was convinced that Louisa was indeed the daughter of the Emperor and she had confided the secret she knew with Dr Johnson and Boswell, both prominent Freemasons. They had made enquiries and said that although those within the Masonic Order were still conflicted on whether it was her, transferring Louisa to France would help to take any potential embarrassment away from them at having failed in their task from the Emperor and would discharge their duties honourably. The confirmation from Florimont-Claude was enough for them to support all Hannah was doing.

Hannah's main efforts were now concentrated on forming Sunday Schools for children and she was growing tired of her London lifestyle and now, once again, spending more and more time in Wrington in Somerset. It meant less and less time in London so her visits to see Louisa were infrequent and dwindled and she contented herself with the occasional report from the hospital, which usually came when more money for her accommodation was required.

With her sisters she worked hard on setting up the schools in Somerset and her writing now mostly consisted of religious tracts and moral tales, which sold very well. The idea of schooling for the poor was not popular with farmers in the area as they felt they would lose the labouring families that they needed to keep the crops growing and the animals looked after.

As a result Hannah and her sisters were now in constant mini battles with farmers and land-owners in Somerset as they tried to establish schools in villages around the Mendips. But even after the battles were won and the schools were established, keeping children coming in when their parents needed their help in the fields was difficult. Eventually she resorted to paying children a penny if they came to the Sunday Schools on every Sunday for a month. The money was welcomed by the families and attendances improved.

- Chapter Eight -

The Last Days

NEWS FROM FRANCE was not good. Many people were starving. The Queen, Marie Antoinette, had been involved in a scandal over the Crown Jewels. She lost popularity with the people, who saw her opulent lifestyle as an insult to them at a time when things were tough.

The project to build an English village at Versailles was being cited as an example of the way she treated her subjects as beneath her. Some country people felt that her plan to dress them in simple clothes and become exhibits in a fake village that she would show off to her high society friends showed just how out of touch she was.

The opulence that she lived in contrasted too much with the poverty of many people in Paris. Against this backdrop time passed by with no news of when Louisa might be collected. Hannah reassured the hospital that she would continue to pay, however long it took.

Hannah was with Mrs Baber, the headmistress of the school she had set up in Cheddar, one day in 1789 when Mrs Baber's grown up daughter Betsy, who assisted her in teaching, came in to say that there was news that the Royal Family in France had been placed under arrest. There was a revolution and much unrest across the channel.

From that moment on Hannah began to suspect that the plan to move Louisa to France would unravel. News of the French Revolution shocked many of her friends in British society, but the biggest discussion was around whether such a thing could happen in London. There were certainly members of the serving classes unhappy enough at the difference between rich and poor who, encouraged by the success of revolutionaries in France, were keen on a similar uprising.

Florimont-Claude Mercy-Argenteau left France for Austria and Hannah arranged a meeting with him. They met in 1793 in London as news of the brutal killing of Marie Antoinette by the guillotine was heard in London.

Florimont-Claude looked gaunt and haggard at the meeting.

"I understand she was humiliated and her body was thrown into a pit. She is absolutely hated in France. There are many agitators here in your own country. London will be next, you mark my words," said Florimont-Claude.

"Peasant protestors broke into Versailles and they set alight the farmhouse and haystack building that was ready for Louisa. The whole project has been abandoned. I fear the Palace will soon be destroyed. It is beautiful but these people have no appreciation of beauty. They are just savages."

Hannah had tears in her eyes. She was always one to weep at conflict and, although she worked tirelessly to help the poor and needy, she could not see how destroying the homes and property of well-off people who often provided the means to help the poor could ever be seen as a positive thing.

"Oh Florimont-Claude, it seems that every day the news is worse and worse and you can see the whole world descending into war and pain and suffering. It is too much for me to even imagine what Marie Antoinette went through. For her life to end in such a brutal and terrible way is unthinkable.

"At first I believed the monarchy could be restored in France but now it seems there is no way back. Thank you so much for coming to see me. I wish it was better circumstances for us to meet."

The pair parted. It was the last time she saw him. The next year she heard that Florimont-Claude Mercy-Argenteau had moved to London to take up a new role as Austrian Ambassador. There were intentions to introduce him to some of her society friends in the capitol, but a few days after his arrival in London news came through that he had died. It seems the strains of the last few years as he had seen those he had served so loyally removed from office and killed by revolutionaries had taken their toll. The secret of Louisa died with him.

Hannah continued the payments to Guy's Hospital but, apart from regular reports that Louisa was a model patient, who mostly sat alone all day, and rarely engaged with anyone, there was little reason for her to bother herself with the Maid of the Haystack. Hannah felt she had discharged her duties. She had tried her best to get to the bottom of the mystery of her background and had raised a great deal of money from friends to help her, but now she seemed to be a hopeless case.

Hannah was paying for Louisa to be kept safely in one of the best hospitals in the country and none of the staff there believed there was any chance of her recovering any of her faculties. She had settled happily into using a bed for sleep.

A Dr Thornton at the hospital worked with a Dr Saunders on trying to find out exactly what afflicted Louisa and what trauma in the past had led to her strange behaviour. One of their team reported that on one occasion Louisa had confided to them that she had been born in Germany and had been married to a man, who served as a Hessian Soldier, supporting the British Army in America.

She said she had travelled to Portsmouth to meet him off a boat when he returned from America. But he told her he had found another woman while he was away. She said, distraught and upset, she had made her way to Bristol and had eventually found comfort in the haystack. The story could not be verified in any way and was simply added alongside all the other tales about her.

After a few years the hospital in Southwark, London, labelled Louisa as an "incurable". Examinations showed that her limbs had contracted from exposure to cold while living outside and by her constant propensity to remain inactive. She became pathetically thin, suffering from arthritis, and was an object of sadness and compassion, looking much older than her years.

That is how the mysterious Louisa saw out her days. The mystery of whether she truly was Royalty - the daughter of an Emperor and half-sister of Marie Antoinette, the last Queen of France - was never solved. She may have been a gypsy dancer, a German runaway whose story somehow got intertwined with that of the Emperor's daughter.

In December 1800 an outbreak of dysentery swept through the hospital. The fragile Louisa became sick and was barely keeping her food down. On the morning of 18th December a nurse went to her bed to wake her. She had passed away in the night.

A message was sent to Hannah More who agreed to pay the expense of her burial in grounds owned by the hospital.

One observer of her story saw her illness as a blessing in her not realising what she had missed out on in life.

As an epitaph he wrote: "After perusing this narrative the intelligent reader will not fail to admire the beautiful dispensation of Providence, in withdrawing from the unfortunate Louisa the gift of reason. Had she retained the faculties of her mind unimpaired, the acuteness of her reflections on the vicissitudes she was destined to undergo, must have embittered her days, and rendered her life almost insupportable. Compared with such sufferings, the poor maniac enjoyed a state of comparative felicity in the indulgence of her childish fancies, and in her insensibility to the woes of her condition. Peace to thine ashes, thou daughter of misfortune, and may thy spirit freed from the encumbrance and the frailties of mortality, taste uninterrupted bliss in those regions where the case of an all-seeing Father provides for the happiness even of his meanest children!"

A month after Louisa's death a poem, written in Bath, and signed W.M, appeared in The Lady's Monthly. It read:

In yonder dust unmark'd for public fame,
Low rests the relics of Louisa's frame!
Poor hapless suff'rer, of the maniac line,
They wrongs no more a tortur'd breast confine
Enough for thee, that ling'ring Sorrow's breath
Found final rescue in the boon of Death!
Tormented they who overwhelm'd with grief!
Accurs'd the crime that 'reft they reason's ray,
Tho' thou be ransom'd for eternal day!
And, where frail innocence would vice repel
May guardian angels thy sad story tell!

In 1815 the body of Marie Antoinette, daughter of Emperor Francis I, was exhumed and given a Christian burial and her remains placed among those of the French Kings in Basilique Cathedral Saint-Denis in Paris.

The body of Louisa, possibly the illegitimate daughter of Emperor Francis I, and born around the same time as Marie Antoinette, lies unrecognised in a pauper grave in London.

About the author and this book

Martin J. Powell

Martin J. Powell is a journalist and writer from Bristol, UK. He first heard about the Maid of the Haystack in the early 1980s while researching local legends for a local history magazine article. Over several decades he sought to find out more about her and attempt to solve the mystery. This book is the result of that research plus theories on what may have connected characters in her story. The author has previously written factual biographies and this is his first work merging fact with story-telling fiction.